VOICES FROM THE ATTIC

VOLUME XXII

Series Editor: Jan Beatty

THE CARLOW UNIVERSITY PRESS

ISBN 978-0-9827639-6-4

"Foreign Dream," from *Collected Poems* © 2005 by Patricia Dobler, reprinted by permission of the estate of Patricia Dobler.

Thanks to:

Carlow University's division of Marketing and Communications.

Lou Boyle for unparalleled leadership;
Sigrid King for incisive mentorship;
Joy Katz, Nancy Kirkwood, Nancy Krygowski, Evelyn Pierce,
Anne Rashid, Ellen McGrath Smith, Sarah Williams-Devereux,
and Lori Wilson for committed teaching;
Lisa Alexander, Tess Barry, Liane Ellison Norman, Evelyn Pierce,
and Sarah Williams-Devereux for generous editing;
Lisa Alexander, Tess Barry, and Sarah Williams-Devereux for
inspired design and planning;
Sarah Williams-Devereux for leadership, resourceful strategy, and
unswerving organization;
Bri Griffith for enthusiastic assistance with editing;

The Madwomen for out-of-the-attic madness.

for Patricia Dobler

Contents

Introduction

Voices from the Attic Volume XXII is the best work from the Madwomen in the Attic Writing Workshops in poetry, fiction, and nonfiction at Carlow University, taught by myself, Joy Katz, Nancy Kirkwood, Nancy Krygowski, Evelyn Pierce, Anne Rashid, Ellen McGrath Smith, Sarah Williams-Devereux, and Lori Wilson.

The Madwomen workshops defy explanation. Yes, I can tell you that there are eight sections of workshops that meet on a semester basis. There are five sections of poetry, two of fiction, and one of nonfiction. I could say that these workshops range in age from 18-94, breathing an exhilarating energy into classrooms of terrific women writers. But then, I wouldn't be telling you about the unstoppable spirit of these women, how they show up week after week out of a love of writing, a commitment to their work, and a joy in each other. No, it isn't all perfect or beautiful—but the Madwomen are all about community, the support of women's work in the world. They *show up* for each other.

One example of this extended community is the developing Madwomen Mentorship program, co-directed this year by Emily Mohn-Slate and Daniela Buccilli. It's a semester-long, free program in which a currently enrolled Madwoman works with an experienced writer in areas such as revision, reading, and publishing. Emily and Daniela developed and nurtured the mentorship program with wonderful results this year.

Also this past year, we celebrated the 2015 Patricia Dobler Poetry Award with a reading by the winner, Amanda Newell, for her poem, "A Woman from the Infant Mortality Review Board Calls." The judge was the poet, Lynn Emanuel. The Dobler Award is awarded to a woman writer over the age of 40 who has not yet published a book. This is a national award, and attracts more women writers each year.

Our *Writers on Writing* program featured a visit by esteemed poet Maggie Anderson, former director of the Wick Poetry Program at Kent State University. In Fall of 2015, we enthusiastically held the first annual Dorothy Louise Holley Memorial Reading, made possible by the generous endowment from Dorothy's daughter, Beth Piraino. We were fortunate to welcome Maggie Anderson as the first reader in this series. We are so grateful for this generous gift by Beth, and to be able to honor Dorothy's work each year. In Spring 2016, the Madwomen Reading Series featured the incomparable Diane Glancy, author of more than 25 books of poetry, fiction, nonfiction, and plays, including her latest book of poems, *Report to the Department of the Interior.*

We have continued our progress with the growth of the Patricia Dobler Dream Fund, the ongoing work of the MadFridays reading series curated by Kayla Sargeson and Laurin Wolf, and MadBooks. MadBooks continues to publish chapbooks and full-length books by featured Madwomen. This year, *The Color of Black* by Beatrice Vasser and *Ordinary Tasks* by Marilyn Marsh Noll were published. Congratulations to Beatrice and Marilyn on their terrific writing. Thanks to editor Liane Ellison Norman and assistant editors Emily Mohn-Slate and Lisa Alexander for their expert work on MadBooks.

The Madwomen have now left the attic, traveling to conferences around the country. Madwomen Tess Barry, Sheila Carter-Jones, Celeste Gainey, Emily Mohn-Slate, and Maritza Mosquera presented a panel entitled, "Attention! Women at Work: Madwomen in the Attic" at the 2016 Split this Rock Festival in Washington, D.C. Also, the Madwomen were presented at the Association of Writers & Writing Programs Conference in Los Angeles, 2016, as part of the panel, "Beyond the Poetry Classroom: Serving the Underserved," along with poet Maria Mazziotti Gillan, Nicole Santalucia, and others. A new program, "Mad Girls," began this year as a collaboration between the Carlow Madwomen and Ellis School in Shadyside. Madwoman Tess Barry has been teaching small group workshops at Ellis and facilitating wonderful connections there.

The Madwomen accomplishments have also grown tremendously, in terms of book and magazine publication, grants and awards, residencies, etc. This is amazing news, and I want to congratulate all the Madwomen for their initiative, determination, and continued progress! Because of the sheer numbers of Madwomen and successes, I can't mention them all here, but I do want to note some new books of 2016: Jen Ashburn, *The Light on the Wall*, Main Street Rag; Nola Garrett, *Ledge*, Mayapple Press; Roberta Hatcher, *French Lessons*, chapbook, Finishing Line Press; Jennifer Jackson Berry, *The Feeder*, YesYes Books; Jill Khoury, *Suites for the Modern Dancer*, Sundress Publications; Kayla Sargeson, *First Red*, Main Street Rag; Arlene Weiner, *City Bird*, Ragged Sky Press, Liane Ellison Norman has two books coming out: *Way Station* by Finishing Line Press and a reissuing of her nonfiction *Hammer of Justice: Molly Rush and the Plowshares Eight*. The play, *Molly's Hammer*, written by Tammy Ryan and based on Liane's book, has been touring theaters around the country.

The Madwomen have clearly busted out of the Attic. I thank all of them for their generous contributions, their goodwill, and their fervor. The selections in this anthology are a testimony to their hard work, their big dreams. They teach me new lessons each year about the nature of living, the madness of art, and the inevitability of change.

—Jan Beatty 2016

Foreign Dream

I don't seem to have even a bit part
in my dreams anymore,
my dreams are mob scenes,
a huge house-party at a stately home,
ok, wait a minute, more like the houses
where I baby-sat as a kid, or an immense
cocktail party in my old college dorm but with men.
Or it's a restaurant-bar somewhere in wartime Germany;
all at the great long table are frightened. It's dark,
a black-and-white film, I can flit in the dark
from face to face. Everyone smokes.
One woman, handsome but no longer young,
says of an absent friend, "She is dangerous."
All the white still faces at the table agree
with this assessment. And suddenly I'm inside
one of these people. I don't know who.
Someone at this table is a version of me.

VOICES FROM THE ATTIC
VOLUME XXII

After Overtime

A green ping of diesel fumes
wears my face while I inhale
slow & steady following an 18-
wheeled grey barrel without
changing lanes or pulling back.
This can't be good for me.
A headache already poking
out from underneath my left eye.
I like it—metallic & prime
rusting half my head
mile marker after mile marker
¾ of the way home.
Getting there, I rattled some
from the ugly day, banging
pots beneath the sink to throw
myself an angry dinner
of half-assed eggs with stabs of cheese
barely melted. The greens I ate plain,
looking for moths in my bowl as I chewed
because once I found one dead
and huge, beige with spots
like a mushroom. It lived its whole life
inside a bag of spring mix until I cut it open
and let the air in.

Burning Rubber

This girl I thought I loved
gave me all of her Xanax to
help me deal with her bad days.
She drove us way out farm roads
to the tight winding, the selfish darkness.
She really could've dumped me
off a back road bridge. Could've slit
my nipple, she bit so hard pushing
back into the passenger seat.
I had to take the wheel so she could
stop driving me away.

Della Does her Duty

Alone in the voting booth and in a sweat, Della studied the ballot.

Of course, the reigning president deserved a second term. He was sheer swagger. While his sniveling allies scrambled to hoard canned goods and build shelters, he'd chortled in the face of nuclear annihilation. He'd earned her vote.

But Harry(et) was no slouch. Della had snickered with the rest of them when she unveiled her campaign. But Harry(et) finally understood that lofty female mandate: man up and be all things to all people. Della admired how Harry(et) had hit the campaign trail all gussied up one day and severely suited the next, even defusing the snarky journalists' pronoun issues by declaring herself a mostly seat-down toilet user, a down home kind of gal. And that gender-inclusive retooling of her name turned out to be a major PR coup.

But Della admired the current president's knack for wrestling searing subjects into tidy lists. His talking points were as slick as the rankings of the world's finest beaches or sexiest men. As he said, infotainment was serious business, a four-syllable force, not the lightweight concept your grandparents knew. She'd have to vote for him after all.

But how much time did Harry(et) have? Her jowls and sags bled through the best camera filters. It was now or never. Still, her get-ups could be weirder than the turbans and togas the leaders of those moonscape-nations sported. The reigning president's suits had gravitas, just a tasteful splash of a tie against stately neutral tones.

But was another four years without a platform a mistake? The president liked to wing it, no style-cramping planks necessary. Harry(et) had responded by rebranding the planks of her platform as legs. "So much more human," she'd confided on all the talk shows. Della considered it silly at first, but now she agreed. It was really great to zero in on Harry(et)'s legs.

Feather boa flapping about her pantsuit, arms flailing in agitated sincerity, Harry(et)'s last speech registered five stars on most watcher websites. Even better, it was brief enough to be published in its entirety. Della had a copy, courtesy of the strident supporters at the polling station's entrance. Maybe Harry(et)'s points weren't as pithy as the current president's, but they encompassed all factions. Della reread it.

"Leg Number One: Yellow Lights. As President, I will install traffic signals everywhere and expand the duration of the yellow light. These mandatory pauses will slow life's hectic pace, and more importantly, give us time to check our smart phones and/or answer the call to prayer. Moreover, this new hands-free driving time will make expensive public transportation obsolete while eliminating the number one threat to our youth: texting-based automobile collisions.

"Leg Number Two: Conductors as Governors. To stimulate non-military spending, I will, through a lottery system, replace half of the state governors with the conductors of major symphony orchestras. Funding for roads and bridges will skyrocket as people flock to concerts and other venues. Arts programs will flood our schools, at least half of them. Muzak in general will improve, enabling shoppers to enjoy the brick and mortar experience, thus boosting the economy's retail sector.

"Leg Number Three: Kegger for Congress. In the innovative spirit of Martin Luther King, Jr., I hereby propose a less-traveled path to a more civil society. Congress will open its new session with a three-day kegger. At its conclusion, members will reach across any remaining aisles and sing Bruce Springsteen's *Born in the USA*. Afterwards, members will either disband, get to work, or shoot each other with legally and/or illegally acquired weapons, depending on individual state's regulations. While I cannot precisely predict the outcome, it will be an improvement. Thank you and God Bless America."

It had to be Harry(et). America was still aglow from last week's Halloween tizzy of tolerance when a kinder and gentler populace had stampeded Costume World for the Harry(et) multi-pack, a rainbow of possibilities in every box, including three wigs and a bonus instructional pamphlet in twelve languages, three of them no longer even spoken.

Then again, the current president had a point about the virtues of phobias. He wasn't a fanatic. Not all phobias are created equal, he'd cautioned, and to forsake our fears is to forsake our nation. The world was a very dangerous place, Della knew.

Incumbent or Harry(et)?

That's when it hit her. Both candidates extolled old-fashioned seat-of-the-pants logic. Della shut her eyes. It wasn't easy, but she managed to submit her ballot without revealing her choice, even to herself. How freeing when the exit pollsters accosted her!

She checked her smart phone. Plenty of time to stock up on non-GMO, gluten-free cheesy poppers and a case of eco-friendly rain forest water. She couldn't wait to arm her security system and sink into her couch to watch breaking coverage of the orderly transfer of power in this great and blessed nation.

On a Night So Beautiful

The guernseys are gone, and weeds
have overtaken the cowpath. This is the farm
where our mother grew up, and from behind
a gnarled walnut tree my brother emerges.
He sits, and rolls a cigarette on his left knee.
I ask him, Do you remember the guernseys?
And he says, Yeah.

The sun goes down and my brother smokes.
A sliver moon and Venus hover over the horizon.
I picture our grandfather walking down the hill
in the bone-white light decades earlier,
his boots kicking the thistles and wild daisies.
One hand holds a milk pail, and the other the leash
to his dog, Louie, who pulls him home.

Chris, I ask, do you remember Louie?
Yeah, he says. I remember Louie.
Then I say, Do you remember the day
we picked berries? And had a picnic
by the creek in the woods? It started to rain,
and we waited out the storm in a run-down corncrib.
He shakes his head, and then I'm not sure
there was a corncrib at all, or berry picking,
but there was definitely a picnic, and rain.

My brother snuffs out his cigarette.
He rises and starts to climb the hill,
away from the house, the barn, the blackcap bushes
where I remember our mother picking berries.
Where are you going? I ask.
Not sure, he says.

His breath and steps grow distant as I gaze
at the moon and stars. Suddenly
I wish I'd asked my brother about his life.
Suddenly I wish I'd told him about mine:
where I'd been, whom I'd loved.
I take out my own cigarettes—stale as chalk
and tasting of licorice—and choke on them
until morning, knowing no one else will stomp
through the weeds to find me. No one else
will bother the thorny brambles or seek the comfort
of dew-soaked pasture grass and clover.
Then I think, How strange to find my brother here,
with our memories so skewed with nicotine
and the spinning of the planets. And on a night
so beautiful it simply asks to be left alone.

My Father does not Remember

He has a grandson who died, that the father
he cries for is dead, does not remember

he once had a wife or where he lives. And sometimes,
more and more, does not remember me.

He lives in the frail husk of his body,
curled in on himself in the womb

of a hospital bed in a room, in a home,
in a southern city.

I think of him as my husband and I watch
a movie, both of us too tired to read,

a story splayed across the TV screen,
of too-easy redemption, a lost father,

a found family, a tied-up-in-a-bow ending.
I think of the man who is no longer my father,

of the last time I heard his voice, the shivering
confusion of its sound—

and I want to take the empty wine bottle
and smash it against my white wall,

send shards of glass flying around our heads,
drops of wine spattering like dried blood.

Surreal Mother

She sounds drunk.
Words slosh and slip,
phrases careen through air,
sentences collapse.
The edges of her eyes melt
as she lies on a bed
in an emergency room,
stares at the pen
in her hand as if it were a lobster,
or a swan, bewildered
as it bleeds blue ink.

She is all splayed legs
and whirling spheres.
Her mythical beast of a brain
furrows and clenches, howls
in its cage of bone.

At Least

When approaching my coffin, the first thing that will strike the viewers will be my hair. Not thinned by age or countless perms, or frizzed after hours under a plastic dome in the beauty salon while my wrinkled claws page through the glossy details of celebrity break-ups, or tapped of color like sap from a maple in winter; my hair will be a blanket of the most vibrant red against the soft silk of my coffin. Some viewers may even glance over their shoulders before sneaking a few fingers over the wooden threshold and touching my smooth strands. The months I've spent growing it out, slathering it with oils and creams, brushing it, and skipping shampoos will all make sense because at least it looks like this today, the last day I will be seen.

I will look like a damn fairy tale princess.

My skin, already pale, will be like the purest marble. It won't hang from my face in bunches or sag into bat wings under my arms. My breasts will stay right where they are, in the middle of my chest, thank you very much. Regardless of their overall purpose, I've only ever asked them to remain there, maybe stay in a bra, maybe sit up a little straighter to attract some attention. They've had a pretty easy life, for breasts. In all, I haven't asked a lot of my body, and the viewers will be able to tell. Flat stomach, no sunburn, still in possession of all limbs and teeth. Skin not pocked by bruises, scars, or hickeys. No one will talk about my beauty in the past tense.

My legs will be varicose-free, if not a little hairy, because the Grand Scheme of Things does not care about my stubble. They will have great muscle definition, because I was exercising like I planned make it to my 70s. Though they will likely be covered in pants, so that particular detail might go to waste. But at least the viewer will be able to see my face. It has been a personal subject of study for my entire life—the first piece of me that I see in the morning and the last thing I take care of at night. I've seen it through scourges of pimples, various scabs, chicken pox, and even a black eye (thanks to my brother and a rogue baseball when I was seven), all to deliver it to this point: framed by red hair and dark wood and white silk. The only hint of wear will be the faintest traces of smile lines; at least they will know that I laughed.

And boy, talk about well-attended. The deli trays and coffee will be gone in a matter of minutes, not taken home to the families of the funeral home staff who will chip it away into lunch portions for the rest of the week. The friends I've made in college won't have drifted away and forgotten about me, too concerned with a daughter's piano recital or a son's graduation, nephew's marriage or the birth of the first granddaughter, until the majority of the names mentioned in the annual family newsletter (attached to the Christmas card containing rehearsed smiles and unfortunate sweaters) are the names of strangers. The grief of my loss will be more than just a passing regret that we hadn't called each other in a few years. The memory of my voice will be as fresh as this morning's weather report.

If I have to go now, at least I won't be overstaying my welcome. I'll be leaving behind an uncomplicated life: no pets to rehome, no children to put into guardianship, no plants to water. No widower. No one can say that I outlasted my potential. I will be more radiant and interesting than ever, and I will be gone.

SAMANTHA BARRETT

On Saying Goodnight to My Mother in Her Eightieth Year

She walks me out to the driveway
her dozens of chimes bumping softly
against one another in late January wind.
They sway back and forth
lit by her kitchen window,
she hugs me and I bend to kiss her.

Touch her hands, her head
to my lips. Her hair grown so white
and soft smells woodsy wind-
blown, smells like home.
I love you Mumma.

I love you bunches, she replies, holds
me in her arms a moment.
Her long drive pitch black,
her trees bare thick shadows
as I make my way through muddy
tire tracks to her yellow-bricked road.

She calls as I walk on, *I love you
daughter*, calls it to me again and again
and I call back to her in kind.
Turn and see her outline recede,
the light of her window

The faint echo of chimes
as I come to the street, her voice
certain when I reach the cobblestones.
I love you more, she sings. I hear
but can no longer see her.

Reading Ochester's *First Brassière*

Turns out it's not a poem about Ed's first bra
or even his breasts but about the cock, rubber-
banded to the adolescent gym-class thigh
and bouncing up and down on buses, a poem
about condoms flying off at ill-appointed moments
like *exhausted birthday balloons.*
And the guy refusing to make it with a naked girl
in a raccoon coat because he's writing
an honors thesis about Wallace Stevens.
Strangely, I have never made it with a man
wearing a condom, never even seen one
up close—though I've seen balloons unknot
and shoot themselves across lawns plenty of times.
But I have worn a bra since I was thirteen,
growing breasts was growing an unfamiliar
tongue, waking in the mouth of someone
I'd never known: never soaped, never
dressed or touched, never comforted
or bled from. That summer everyone stared.
Hot, giant fans blowing circles of air down
my back as I returned from communion.
People turned their heads as I passed,
looked at me like I was injured—but accusatory,
like I had no one to blame but myself:
their eyes furtive, ashamed of my reddening.
I was wearing a white skirt,
Saturday evening mass,
I was going to the carnival that night.
I told my friends to go on
without me. In the church Ladies,
I scrubbed my bloody skirt and peered
into the fuzzy glass above the sink.

TESS BARRY

I felt the red of carefree days
run through my hands and down
the yellowed drain, felt myself recede.

At Poets House: Remembering Muriel Rukeyser

I was born the same year Rukeyser gave birth
to her son William & my mother's frequent threat
was to disinherit me:
                           for registering Peace & Freedom,
leaving home before I married, doing anti-war work in L.A.
then moving up to Berkeley. I was lucky:
always my mother would relent, after the requisite tears.

I wonder: What got Muriel disinherited by her father?
Editing that leftist journal at Vassar? Arrested at 21
while covering the Scottsboro trial in Alabama?
Raising her son alone, as an outlaw-unwed mother?
That she was a gadfly, a bisexual, a Marxist, a poet?

It's a wintry 100th birthday party in Manhattan
with Rukeyser's favorite rum raisin ice cream,
Dunhill cigarettes & whiskey.
                                    Everyone's here:
her son William, biographers, poets, editors,
old lefties. I study the squint lines
behind Alicia Ostriker's gold-rimmed glasses,
Gerald Stern's stooped gait & steady voice
& whisper Rukeyser's words:

What would happen if one woman told the truth—

In 1978, Muriel hoped to give a talk on "Lesbians
in Literature," but was too ill. By 1980, she was dead
of a stroke, two years younger than I am now.

In teaching, her favorite prompt was: *I could not tell*
Look how the words leap from her poetry:

child woman Orpheus bird suicide touch song you

JOAN E. BAUER

Tumbleweeds

On the highway south of Los Banos, the signs:

Water = Jobs   *Congress Created Dustbowl*

Amid walnut trees, peach orchards & apricots
already evidence of drought.

By the time we're in Coalinga,
the tumbleweeds are everywhere

I try to do my part: conserve water.
Bathing only every other day.

*

Tumbleweeds remind me of country music
& desolation.

Maybe you think of that ultimate
Stoner's band of the 1990's all retro-grunge,

recycling Blue Öyster Cult for inspiration.

Maybe you think of the *The Big Lebowski*,
that first scene.

My Dad was Alive the Last Time I Ate Chinese Take-Out

I can now answer half
of the slip of a fortune,
but couldn't then: *How dark*

is dark? How wise is wise?
Worms on the cross section
of brain scan, white, opaque,

not what you'd think of as dark,
but dark still, like blood
in the tube, rust-red,

old rusty blood suctioned
each time he'd start to struggle
& breathe over the vent,

gag reflex his only strong reaction,
though cancer was reacting,
lighting up meninges on the scan,

glowing spiders bright,
giving up brethren hiding
in dark holes in his right lung,

those who spun webs north.
Wise to not want to know?
Was he wise to not want to know?

[m]other's dream

husband a bongo drum   all bang & hollow
      round   unclothed
leading me
the path to our bedroom   carpet of ladybugs
         a wave

spotted foam circles my feet

your house is on fire your children alone

children look like a road
        cross-legged on a mattress on the floor
        all wearing valentine red

i open
my hands
behind his
back release
two butterflies
people i
know but
aren't the
faces of

At Sixty

As I move through city streets
My skin transparent, white
Like a cold sky
There is no canopy
Or covering, no strategies left
To block the gaze of others
From seeing
I am not really human
But like a blind mole rat
Born hairless with red eyes
Frightened of fast-moving steel
And concrete forms that impede my flight
From predators
Who sense weakness
I can't hide anymore

MARY BIANCHI

You (for Isabelle)

Darling dearest sweet one my love,
it has always been you.

You were heralded by a red-headed bird,
the insistent woodpecker who flew by me in the garden.
Back and forth past my car
trying to tell me about you.

In that same garden
where my roses succumbed inevitably to black spots,
I was finally struck by the realization of you.

Palm trees, mosquitoes waited for you.
After twenty-four weeks I viewed you through a porthole
in the incubator, bells 24-hour piercing light.

And you felt the war we waged despite you,
you entered this group, this unhappy place
we had made, and tagged along. Old soul

Baby my love do you know how sorry I am
that you don't know my pride in you?
That you have survived the battles we fought;
your father's escape into death?

I remember hitting you.
My rage without clear targets.

I remember neglecting you.
My attention on the more important.

I remember reminding you
how disappointed I was in you.

But remember all the birds I showed you willow trees peonies
the leaves we studied and the skies when they turned pink?
Flowers pulled off the stems—
because you are the perfect embodiment of all we have loved together.

Glorious child when you leave part of me will die.

MARY BIANCHI

September 1966, an excerpt from the novel
Borrowed Light

Maggie looked up. The sky sang blue, a bright clear blue: azure. Only a word with a *z* would do for this blue—a blue of possibilities. Dazzle another *z* word good for today. She would write them down when she got home.

The snap in the air created bursts of energy with every breath. She felt her cheeks glow. Exhilaration was what it created. She let the brightness envelope her and looked at the trees in the distance. They stood straight and tall against the bright sky making red and golden layers up the hills. The sidewalks winked white with glitter. Around the bend on Castle Shannon Boulevard she heard the car tires hum over the cobblestones. Everything seemed light.

Only her books were heavy: Biology, Algebra 1, and French 1, stacked atop her three-ring binder. The binder was one of her few possessions new and hers from the start. Its fabric cover was the faded gray-blue of a winter sky. Rough to the touch, it left its woven imprint on her wrists. Inside it, a big brass clip with teeth held her schedule overtop a rectangle where she had neatly written her name and address in her best cursive, the capital *M* and *K* strokes looping like candy canes as she had been taught:

Margaret Kelly
Baptist Home Orphanage
Crystal Drive
Pittsburgh, Pennsylvania

At school on other students' binders she noticed doodled designs done in blue Bic pen. Girls fashioned big square initials—their own or a boyfriend's. Maggie kept hers clean and new. Her bad foot dragged a bit behind, though she could keep up a good pace. Straight home each day, the rules, nowhere else to go anyway. No one else to walk with since the others from the Home were still in junior high or even younger. Hard to push her glasses up better on her nose while carrying her books, so she tilted her chin up to counter-balance them sliding down.

She passed the apartment building with the trim-like icing, her favorite in the row, its zigzag designs made from different colored bricks. Zigzag. More z's. She could imagine living there someday in the top floor apartment with its sloped roof. She would write her books beneath the eaves and look out the little leaded glass windows that glinted in the sunlight.

She passed the duplexes. She heard doors slam, first car doors in a driveway, then the thud of a big front door, someone home. She passed the laundromat with its smell like the smell of the laundry room at the orphanage, laundry one of her jobs. Another curve, the hum of tires, shouts and laughter of some boys from across the street behind her. She quickened her step. Come on, old foot. She heard a whistle like for a pretty girl.

"Hey Maggot!" The yelling started.

She hugged her heavy books. The day went dark in her head.

"Maggot, Maggot, Maggot!" they chanted.

Her pulse echoed in her ears.

"Going home to find some dog shit for dinner, Maggot?"

She tripped over uneven concrete on the sidewalk. Her glasses shifted off one ear. Her books tumbled. Her binder fell and sprawled open, the rings split wide. Papers fluttered like white wings. She stooped and tapped them down, fumbled to get the rings closed. They scraped her cold fingers.

"Can I carry your books, Maggot?" Said with high-pitched sweetness, mocking. Jeers of laughter from across the street faded as the voices turned away down Cooke Lane.

She shifted to her knees. Tears fogged her glasses in the chilly air. She reached to gather her scattered books, tried to brush a glob of mud from the cover of her binder with her fingers. It smeared across the middle. She picked it up and clutched it to her chest.

Flying Fortresses

From my kitchen window I see about thirty starlings
lined up on the ridge of the barrel-tiled roof
three houses down.

They take off in formation soaring like B-17s,
their lead bird guiding them through
flight maneuvers.

Preparing for descent, they form a wide arc
before gliding back to the launching pad,
wings tilted in the exact same pattern.

They wait awhile,
then head out for their next mission.
They clock about ten sorties an hour.

Maybe tomorrow, I'll look out and see P-51 Mustangs
flying in to protect the B-17 Flying Fortresses
from enemy bombers.

Organ Concert At Calvary Church, 2014

For my daughter, Mia

The setting sun finds the rose window.
Prisms of color dot the stone.
Thunderous sounds of Widor's Toccata
Allegro Vivace all stops out fill the space.
I ride the wave of sound, out of my thoughts,
around and through the Gothic arches,
toward the jewel tones violet red and green.
Wishing you no pain, no cough, no nausea.
Just beautiful colors and sounds.

GERRY ROSELLA BOCCELLA

Julia

At five o'clock, the attorney across the street
runs her 3k addiction every morning regular
as my first cup of coffee. I can't help but think
of you, Julia, the way you filled that blue velour
track suit, how we rail-thin siblings used to call you
piggy. Still, you were the one of us who wouldn't
sit on the bench at swimming class, who didn't lie
and say you had your period. You weren't afraid
to let the water and the chlorine take the straight
back from the straightening comb.
You didn't run from your curvy hips or your nappy hair
even then in the years when we'd heat the hot-comb
on the gas stove's burner, moisten our bushy hair
in pomade, singe it straight. The lift of my breasts
in the cheap training bra slowed me the last time
I ran a five-yard dash in high school gym
as I slumped my shoulders to hide from them.

Lemington Avenue, 1960

Downstairs, lights bounce from glass ornaments,
tinsel, the talk of the grown people when they think
we aren't near.
At the top of the stairs, I angle my spindly legs
to the banister on New Year's Eve, hear
the sitter's words,
my fifteen-year-old cousin, in my head:
Doralee, little girls are best seen and not heard.
I watch the dancers to Motown, jazz, Jimmy McGriff.
Ricky, our nineteen-year-old neighbor
with the cinnamon skin grabs Miriam's waist,
she—the tallest woman
in the room and unfashionably dark—
stumbles back a little
in pink satin t-straps on her mannish feet.
Next year, Ricky won't come here.
He'll be at Slim's, his hangout on Homewood Avenue,
when John, who was already working the steel mill
the year Ricky was born,
drunk, warns Ricky away from his wife.
Ricky, laughing, will turn his back,
say, *Old man, get on out of my face.*
John will return with a Smith & Wesson.
At the wake, Ricky's mother will say
she dreamt she was mopping
blood, buckets of blood.
But, tonight, Ricky sees me,
grabs me and tosses me up high,
holds me up to the hallway dome light
and says, *See, when I hold you up to the light
like this, you're not so dark.*

DORALEE BROOKS

Black Cutouts

Black cutouts on a green silent field.

I hold my scissors, cut elongated squares, trapezoids.

4 legs that dangle free, 4 anchor hooves to keep them solid—

& I paste.

Sticky-fingered, I cut out heads—triangles, like isosceles, scalene,

& I think—

up & down, up & down

stationary seesaw grazers.

On a slope of green they shift, move higher, face a morning sun,

& I paint swashes of red and orange, some violet—

changes coming.

6:45am, roadside

On my way to work:
salty roads, a dusting of snow, and Christmas vacation is over.
It's 23° cold and I'm up Erzen's hill, rounding the bend.
Past the park, and in the long stretch, I'm goin back down the other side—

& way down there, on the right, a tiny figure—

A grey hoodie zipped up tight, and long dark hair tucked in.
Eyes closed and head bobbing, a wild and tender smile carved deep.
Arms are swinging and feet are moving to some cloudless gypsy rhythm—
his own mysterious dance.

Roadside and waiting,
that's Daniel.

Evening Closes Comprehension

The last birds to feather the moon
steal dreams of redundant loss.
They pluck names from Tuesday's eyes,
wipe silent Wednesday's lips with sharp-beaked tongues.

Tomorrow, they leave their bony wings
outstretched on morning's clock-like face,
for me to wrap and throw away
with empty cups and dirty plates.

Last night

it rained bells and pearls.
Today, we go tripping down the street.

After confetti, the sky closes.
Internal song pastes words together with paper tears.

Your stories are not for the cat's pink floral ears.
Put food in her bowl, and go to bed.

Origami Bridges

Like a soul removed from my body, I watch
I see
I am swollen with a soup of emotion
I watch
The miracle of a gift
My son
He is eight and sits crisscross style
On the floor by the dogs
Studies and folds
He is absorbed in *his* art
His concentration does not falter
His silhouette, I can glimpse
While I work in the kitchen

Our family splinters sharply in chaos
Our home feels jailed by a rain cloud necklace
His hand outstretched
It's an origami masterpiece
This time a bear
"Oh that is exquisite," I say, pulling him close to kiss his head
The frog, the rhinoceros, the rose and the dragonfly
I saw it all fall loose
Many more paper masterpieces were made that year
As I go downstairs to the pantry for supplies
I am reminded
There, the clear zippered bag that once housed a blanket
One hundred presents plus of brightly colored folded art

Red Brocade

Some days he stares at the chair,
as if he can't imagine it without his wife.
A red brocade, elegant in its day,
antique parlor chair from my father's father's home.
My father speaks to the chair,
I tilt it forward, to demonstrate
the emptiness.
His eye could be the space of a lost house—
same hard floor, same voices,
as if he just waked from a cardboard town
where no one knows his name.
Daze enters his eyes again.
Even street signs, prank-twisted,
twist the turns he once knew by heart.
Pale, the familiar rags of memory. Where he was
the day the tall tree fell, or when
red brocade moved to my house from his,
the one house he remembers.

GAYLE R. CARROLL

Yellow Pencil

Minions of yellow leaves fall,
wind-bruised and floating down from storms assembling,

like big-feet troops, lining up for perdition.
I watch, I listen. Become a child submerged,

the aftermath of war, not
knowing what war's about. But loving

dry leaves falling, that rustle and whisper.
My steps scuff on the cracked concrete walk to school.

Numbers, words, beginning to burble,
a yellow-brick stew newly settling in.

Pressing ahead, I believe in tomorrows, years.
A big-foot kid ankle deep in leaves speaking.

One step, another— I'm eager, and proud—
a whispered fear and grace.

What moves I know, what words—
dip pen, blank white pages. Numbers to add and subtract.

Figures I form, one by one. My chewed yellow pencil
writing words into stories.

Hammer

Back in the day they called a good-looking woman
a hammer—a woman of terrifying beauty.

Just looking at her could knock a man's head
into another hemisphere. Like Medusa—turn a man
stone cold. Crazy dead in his tracks.

There's another kind of hammer. It has a hemispherical
head and is used to deliver blows. The three-dimensional
solid head, hard face type is what her husband used.

Said he kept the ball-peen under the bed for protection.
Dense volume of forged steel could not comprehend
the simplest reason.

Forceful man with his authoritative penis, claimed insanity.
Couldn't remember meditating the moment. Like
the moment she said, *It's over*—the moment he reached

for the hammer, the moment her naked body went down,
the moment her brain was exposed and he could see she
had been thinking how to tell him the uncomplicated way.

No crime of passion equation was needed to gauge punch force,
to determine number of blunt ball-peen blows that equal—*until
death do us part.*

Lovely Boys

Near dusk all these boys,
these lovely boys stand twisted as shadows.
I love me some shadows that stand as boys

so when the black comes, it comes
with a hushed mouth. Says, *shush*.

Come night these lovely boys—black ones,
neon ones, iridescent ones light up alive
and I fall headfirst into

dark rhythms that plug holes in my lungs
leave breath enough only to weep
a broken down love song for these

lovely boys whose shortness of breath is quick
like pigeons flit to sleep in tops of trees where
nighttime hunters cannot

reach them—on ledges and roof tops, in nooks
and cracks, behind signs where nobody ever sees
and come light

there they are, pretty picture on a bill board,
their city sneakers strung over the telephone wire
heavy as tree limbs with fruit

without feet the left shoe is always a step higher
than the right, but both are black as burnt twigs
against new day sun

the shoestrings braided in a knotted pattern
of static hip-hop, balance the pair like a body
hanging as a butchered thing.

Three Black Boys

Three black boys
saunter down the street
in summer's browning heat
through a neighborhood
where people grimace
with their teeth,

but no one dares to speak to them.

Haunted by the searing sun
I watch the games the boys run
Without a ball   how they play
all through the night and all day

on the corners of the streets
that take them.

Riding in my air-conditioned car
I look at them from afar
I too a child of blatant tar
Can't begin to reach them.

you are like candy

the kind I crave at night
a hard sweet button
unwrapped
brought to my mouth

your taste   my tongue
a dance of
butterscotch-bourbon
dissolves

Thin Ice

This is the velvet moment
when deep darkness lifts
across the river
along the ridge of the hills beyond.

Perched on the eastern tip
of Sycamore Island
hugging the shoreline,
a flush of mallards
breaks out of the tight huddle
that has kept them warm and alive
overnight in sub-freezing temperatures.

They're ice skating. One-by-one,
like school children in single file formation,
each duck slowly waddles out on the fragile ice
that has formed around water's edge.

Overhead, a cloud floats by, palest gray
flowing into ripe peach. One duck slips through the ice,
as if she forgot to look where she was going.

Nearby Canadian geese awake, leisurely float
around as if to greet them, and perhaps suggest
that new ice is thinnest and not to be trusted.

Unfurled

A great blue heron landed at river's edge this morning.
Perhaps our summer-in-autumn weather made her bold
and the promise of a bath was irresistible.
She unfurled her wings like a seraphim,
then dipped her slender neck,
splashing as she drew it back toward her body.
Some distance away,
a fish hawk plunged into the water,
flying off with its catch.

Birds and Breakfast

A pair of cardinals plunder
freshly planted sunflower seeds
chirp to each other
soft sounds over breakfast.

Winona, my friend of 40 years,
visits for a few days on her way
to a senior living place in Colorado.
Her brain betrays her/frontal lobe aphasia/
words won't come/feet shuffle.

Fog rises from the muddy Monongahela.
Yesterday's storms broke trees
moisture clings to everything.
Tomato plants and basil leaves drip.

We sit at the kitchen table, try to talk.
Like the fog over Pittsburgh
mistiness in her head
stifles her voice
slows her movements.

I am losing another friend.
Another person who knows
my faults and foibles,
loves me anyway.

KAY COMINI

Birthing Spring

Sixty-one inches of snow and counting.
Yesterday was 65 degrees and sunny.
I woke today to rain and falling temps.
It is supposed to be in the single digits tonight.
Snow again tomorrow.
When a child is coming out of my body
I cannot imagine that the pain will ever end.
The mind knows it will be done eventually
but the body writhes.
Yesterday, when the snow melted
and I didn't need gloves or scarf
I imagined my flower garden—
in shades of lavender and pink.
They're predicting hail this afternoon
the head is crowning.
Today, my world is dilated to ten.
I imagine holding my child
get my down jacket back out of storage.

Seaside, Oregon

After "Paradise, Indiana" by Bruce Snider

One overcast night the ocean crossed me
    at any little Northwest coastal town

with simple names like Seaside or Oceanside,
    the Pacific blowing its bitter wind

over a bright lighthouse in the dark.
    That's the beacon, sailors say, *the guide*

that brings us home: the small town tranquil,
    fresh fish gutted, anchored boats

tug on cut off trees, with heavy
    trunks, near a neon sign flashing Pirate's Grub.

The seaside pub packed with tourists,
    salmon grilling over coals. My girlfriend

sighed a full gut across the dinner table, I leered
    at a hungry gull drift over retreating

tide. While we ate close to the bar fireplace, love
    devoured its burn. It went on,

the night we decided to call off our engagement,
    forget how you said it was the real thing.

Like dead starfish sinking into sublime blue
    where we threw our whole

hearts out to wild sea, our dreams sank
    with a thousand drowned skeletons

ANGELA CORNELIUS

along the Oregon coast, *The Graveyard of the Pacific*,
  mariners say, A Lee Shore—no safe

haven, where all nature's forces conspire
  to wreck you, like the New Carissa

that crashed off Coos Bay in 1999. I could feel the weight
  of the sunken bones call me to the ocean

edge. I remember the night the moon was so bleak,
  the stars brightened in their shining, the depths

lit up a cosmic sky, indigo-colored and sparkling.
  I pointed at our constellations,

held your hand with drunken abandon,
  we rambled the craggy brink together.

Found and flung promise rocks, now forgotten
  on ocean floor, their surface so covered in seaweed

you might say, if seen at sunrise, green turquoise.

Cain Misses the Mark

The boy's swollen lip twists around his smile.
How the doctors called him brave,
the nurses barely restraining him
while they stitched the ragged edges.

In the equation of motherly love, the expressions
are never equal. One slice of pizza ever so slightly
larger; one longer moment lingering over a bedtime story.

The battle plays out on the playground.
The swing becomes a disc hurled by a brother
aiming for a medal he cannot not win.

A jawbone averts the moment of impact,
offering instead the lip that once closed
around my breast. Now it is cleaved
and sure to be scarred,
worn like a medal, hard won.

Pilgrimage

Once we went on a pilgrimage
with rusty bones, short tempers
and no muse.

Your soft hand on my cheek,
a spring tendril inching its way
through dark loam—

You were a good-hearted man
who thought the world of me

But I sliced the air with my own cruel sickle—
sharp stubble poking at your eyes.

If I rewrite the scene
you will stand with outstretched arms;
I will spread thorn-less roses at your feet.

Instead, my road leads away from you,
my blood-soaked boots
discarded along the path.

ELISABETH CRAGO

A Fish Story: Veterans Day at McCormick & Schmick's

While we sleep, Armageddon strikes our fish.
The sidewall of their wet world cracks open
like a California earthquake. It spills
to the floor, through the floor, waters the buds
of pink flowers on the dining room wall,

creeps across our daughter's bedroom floor,
finds the fastest route to the chandelier
below. *Save the fish!* Our kid shouts in tears.
They squirm in the last drops of life. We dump
them in a bucket of spigot water,

rush them off to the mercy-on-pets place.
The insurance guy swallows his laughter,
doesn't bother to come take a look.
We love our new wallpaper, don't replace
the fish jail. Try luscious trout dressed in nuts.

Enough

Along the shoreline, I see it,
opalescent against the sand,
fragment of shell.

As children, we heaped plastic buckets
with summer wonders,
unable to choose just one,
sure that more was all.

Intent on shape, form, and color,
unknowing, we found beauty
in fragile pieces of some other wholeness.

A lifetime later,
breathing deep another summer,
I reach for this one scrap of shell,
frayed, yet flawless.

If ancient forests fall

cypress logged (burned) to their knees
the language of egrets silenced, no more
the rhythm of the pecker, the alligator's
slimy soup & salad, verdant green swamp
gone—hiding claws and scales and bulging
eyes of diamond yellow

then what of the Wood Stork, and her baby
like apparitions floating white just to the right
of the boardwalk, fashioned from bald cypress,
slithering through this Corkscrew preserve like
a Burmese python—markers like gravestones
naming the vanished

Living with Lizards II

Under a lounge chair by the pool
the smallest one drinks the dripping drips
from my Sydney's wet bathing suit.

Earlier she'd vacuumed out the car:
Guess what I found? My lost glasses, I'd hoped.
No a lizard, a living lizard underneath the seat!

My first flirt in Florida was lizard, lunch courtyard
our eyes met, 90 degrees, his throat sac throbbing.
In Italy, I was known as Lizard Killer, whacking walls

with a broom to chase them out, from statue stance
to full sprint at 18 miles per hour, lizards everywhere
on the stair, in my hair, under the toaster there's a tail.

Lizards gossip, so be careful of what you say, and once
I saw one on a rock with hundreds of listeners:
the lizard holding court: Monday morning.

Sea Monsters and Sirens, LTD.

Ava scanned the ten pages of the document, unable to identify a single word within the tiny text. No matter. Ava signed above the signature line labeled *Employee.*

"I have one more place for you to initial," the SMS sales recruiter said, pointing to a paragraph on the third page.

"By initialing here you confirm that you are aware that as terms of your employment and as an effect of the beta implant, you will never return to former residences, former places of employment, businesses, etcetera, nor will you initiate any contact with family, friends or acquaintances."

Ava initialed with a flourish and handed the document back. "All yours."

"Transportation will arrive at the portico in a half hour." The recruiter rose, leaving her alone in her room.

She laid back on her bed and shut her eyes. During the first month of rehab she fantasized about contacting her parents. As time went on she cared less and less. SMS's contract ensured she would never have the chance. Ava alienated everyone she knew, owed landlords all over town money, and the longest she held any job was a month. She wasn't sure how the SMS recruiter located her and while his offer seemed too good to be true, the cash signing bonus sucked her right in, hook, line, and sinker. Prostitution was in her future if she didn't clean herself up. SMS guaranteed a job upon completion of a six-month company-sponsored rehab program. She had nothing to lose. The food was great and while required to drink an algae-laden "cleanser" each day, there wasn't much expected of her other than a weekly blood draw. It was like no detox she ever heard of but it worked. She spent each day poolside, working on a killer tan.

Finally it was time to go. She joined six other women in the limo bus waiting in the drive. They were all ex-addicts like herself who she met poolside. Ava chose a window seat and after the bus traveled a few miles down the road, nodded off.

DONNA DZURILLA

On the first day Ava spent hours in pain, overwhelmed as she absorbed and processed multitudes and variations of color—many she had never seen before. On the second day, she found color and warmth in all directions while a soft, barely perceptible rhythm rocked her. She became part of her surroundings, no longer aware of time passing. She simply was. She no longer had words.

The next day she discovered a smooth surface—one she was unable to pass through—and it jarred her. Frustrated she tried again and again to penetrate this *limitation* until a sharp brightness blinded her to everything except the beautiful creature on the other side. The creature froze. She reached towards it, and it reached back. Ava jerked back, and it did, too, and then, with a first taste of fear, she wriggled up and away, terrified as her own reflection joined to her as she skimmed along the smoothness.

Condoms and Commies

During dinner, Daddy moved Mother's latest floral centerpiece to the side so he could see whether everyone was eating. Mother wasn't.

"For the love of Christ, Eleanor, aren't you going to eat?" Mother wasn't being herself lately and often cried for no reason. Now she got up and ran into the kitchen. The swinging door wonked shut behind her, almost putting out the dining room candles. I followed her. In the kitchen Mother was leaning over the stove, catching the tears in her Tuesday hankie.

"Are you worried about Bob? Is that what's wrong?"

"No honey. Bob is all right. I'm sure he's all right." She tried to smile. What kind of smile was that? I recognized it right away—it was the smile through tears, like in the war movies.

Then something gave me the nerve to say it. "You're in love with Bob, aren't you?" It had been the look in her eyes when I spied her returning that "thing" to him—the condom she'd stolen out of his uniform pocket, *my* boyfriend's military uniform pocket. I really loved Bob, even if he was too short for me. He wasn't going to use it or anything, with her always breathing down our backs.

"Are you in love with him? Tell the truth. And where did you put the argyle socks I've been knitting for him? Where?" She didn't answer. The leftover mashed potatoes were turning a virid color against the sides of the aluminum pan. Her movements seemed too automatic. I thought about how she'd kept acting like he was *her* date the last time he was home on leave. I gave up waiting for an answer and marched back into the dining room.

Dad was looking down at his plate, forcing himself to chew. It was so quiet I could hear snowflakes pelting against the windows. Sounds of Mother in the kitchen were muffled.

"What's wrong with your mother?"

"Nothing. I'm going upstairs."

"What about dessert?"

"I don't want any." Dad hated to hear how we didn't want food, especially on Chocolate Dump Cake Night. When weather trapped Mother in the house, she usually made chocolate cake.

Up in my room I sat down at my desk and started to write Bob a letter, but I didn't know what to say, and the flowered writing paper ended up in my Little Orphan Annie wastebasket. Outside, the soft way the snow fell was comforting. With snow on the roofs, little squares of it facing this way and that, our neighborhood could have been one of Dad's miniature railroad scenes. Poor Dad, though. Next morning he'd be out there early, nearly buried by the "dang-gal-darn" stuff, tire chains in hand and the sound of whirring tires everywhere. Wishing he could be somewhere else, anywhere else—especially now.

Did they have winter in Korea? I got out another piece of paper and forced myself to write. Bob's feelings were more important than mine. A good Christian didn't let a soldier down, especially when that soldier had written that he'd killed the enemy with a bayonet. I'd looked up "bayonet" in the dictionary. The newsreels never showed this. They only showed the blasts and the injured bodies. Where were the trumpets? The marching bands? It was all just too depressing.

Dear Bob, Did you ever hear of the commandment Thou shall not kill?

I never wrote this. I wrote about the argyle socks, not mentioning how I suspected Mother of hiding them. Then I remembered that we were supposed to ask the boys questions. Oh yeah, like how is the war?

Actually it wasn't supposed to be a war; it was only supposed to be a conflict. The Korean Conflict. Anyway, when I started with the questions, they just kept coming: Why is my father so mad at us for wasting food? Is he afraid the Communists will take it away? What do army rations taste like? Is the domino effect true? If one person becomes Communist, does that mean everyone else will? And what exactly is it, anyway? The way some people describe it, it sounds so…Christian. Everyone having the same things, what's so wrong with that? No one mentions the subject at school. When are you coming home? Yours truly, Alice.

Later that month my friend June and I went to a matinee of *Gone with the Wind* at The Fulton. Fifth Avenue seemed so drab after the burning of Atlanta. I'd rather have been in Korea where at least something exciting was going on. The slush from the cars was just ruining our camel hair coats. And June, still under the spell of Clark Gable, finished the day off perfectly by asking, "Do you think Bob is ever coming home?"

How could she? People were coming home; this wasn't the World War.

June stayed over and discovered the argyle socks and knitting needles peeking out from under the dust ruffle of my bed. Mother's way of returning them? Why couldn't I have a normal Mother? Or Father, for that matter. Or maybe it was impossible to expect anything normal anymore.

ALICE FUCHS

Spring Not

I am not ready for
spring green hope and bird song,
or blue skies, warm, or sun
shine,
rain on
daffodils or
peepers throbbing in the night.

I am stiff and sore and
reluctant and
my winter quilts hold me
close.

Spring is for copulation and celebration and
I am done with all that.
My hands lie curled in my lap.
They are gnarled.
They are empty.
They have done enough.

This year I will not till the soil or
bake the bread or diaper the babies or
caress the man, no.

I dream in wisps of memories
of my time, gone by,
lived well and enough,
I think it was enough,
and what does it matter anyway?

I am not sad.
I am just finished,
and that is alright.

I will be still,
like these mountains,
worn and weary,
mossy and green.

Poked

my eye in first grade
with a mechanical pencil.
Miss Jackson asked,
are you okay?
I told her *yes*,
but my eye, soaked
in soreness, screaming,
talking back to me…
Miss Jackson asked again,
are you sure?
My seesaw voice said *yes*.
I wanted to ignore my eye
but it was the uncomfortably quiet
room full of people, throats pounding,
waiting to say *this is awkward*, but I thought
this is better than having to
walk the hallway with a fireball eye,
than having to talk about it.
All I wanted to do was bathe
in the silence, not answer questions,
not even my own body could
leave me alone, the last thing
I wanted was to be asked
about the hurt
disguised in small yeses.

September Sounds Like Cancer

Now
you sleep
beneath
dirt curtains,
dirt
where your bones
used to crack in
the morning—
elbows,
kneecaps,
back packed with
dirt.

Now
September
sounds like
cancer,
sounds like the
*

beep
*

beep
*

beep
*

of the ICU heart monitor,
the emptying
of fluid-filled
pockets,
the ones
that (once) sat

full under your
eyes until you
closed them
one
last
time.

Inner City Dreams

That mountain
darkens the light of the moon.

You could be free there.
We could be free.

The wind and rain to help us sleep.
I want to be free there.

Catching drops of water.
Please let them fall on me.

The wind and rain to help us sleep.
That's what you said.

To live for you and me
and be free.

ALEXIS HARRELL

Pawley's Island, South Carolina

That's where my dad's from.
I can see him as a child just running
along the shore.
Scooping up crawdads and
throwing them in the
bucket.

His hair; matted and uncombed.

Yeah that's him
all bare foot with ashy legs.

Today he'll pick some berries—
two for the bucket and three for him.
Crawdads and berries
buckets of 'em
he'd say.

An excerpt from a novel-in-progress

I hid behind a potted plant in the hallway and watched people arrive. Bones, the mailroom guy from my dad's office, gave his wife the pen and stood nervously jangling coins in his suit pocket while she bent over the desk and signed the guest book. She was big, soft and doughy, in a purple, crushed velvet dress. Bones sunk his brown fingers into the luscious flesh above her elbow to guide her into the viewing room. Her tight sleeves and pillowy arms reminded me of the split in a Pillsbury crescent roll package as you bang it on the edge of the counter and the raw dough bursts through the seams with a whispery sploosh.

"I'm hungry," I said to my sister Nancy when she found me in the hall.

Our brother joined us in our hiding place, away from the crowded rooms, away from the awkward encounters with adults and the horrified mute staring of other children.

When our sister Ginnie found us malingering, she put her hands on her hips and said, "Oh brother." She tugged on a set of closed double doors across the hall and they swung wide open, drawing us into a shadowy, empty viewing room. She shut the double doors behind us, muffling the sound of the crowded funeral home, making it far away and of no consequence.

Vases of wilting flowers lined the room. The brightness of the day blazed in a hot, white light at the edges of the drawn dark drapes, but otherwise the room was gray, gloomy. There was no casket, just an empty space where it had been, and yet we stood before it in a line, our hands clasped across our fronts in the posture we had just learned.

Suddenly Ginnie grabbed a lily from one of the vases and lay down on the floor between the banks of flowers. "Okay," she said arranging her skirt in a wide arc. "Let's play funeral." She pointed the lily at Gil. "You're my grieving husband," she said. "Who's a prince, No! A king! And you two," she swung the lily like a scepter in a wide circle indicating Nancy and me, "are my twin princess daughters. Okay? Now everybody come up, one at a time and say the saddest thing you can think of." She lay back down, clutched the lily to her chest, and closed her eyes.

Gil quietly popped the flower heads off a bouquet and mimed that Nancy and I should do the same. Now, each of us with our hands full of decapitated flowers, stood before the fallen queen. Gil raised his hand and silently counted down to three. We opened fire and pelted the deceased. Ginnie leapt up swinging the lily like a bat, and we screamed and laughed and fled from her.

Hallelujah, we'd raised the dead!

I was stunned at how quickly and completely we shed the cowl of grief, as though we'd tossed off the heavy robes that had been laid upon our shoulders and sprang from their smothering darkness into the light.

Ginnie clunked Gil on the back of his head; lily petals tumbled to the ground, and a streak of pollen painted the back of his black jacket. "You're on my side," she said, pointing at me.

Each side set up camp behind the rows of flowers flanking the room. Roses, carnations, bachelor buttons, and giant chrysanthemums flew across the room and, on impact, exploded in showers of petals. Spider mums had the most impressive blast pattern and the generals, Gil and Ginnie, were willing to risk their troops, Nancy and me, to acquire them. I crawled behind the vases to the end of the display where a whole vase of Spider mums stood at the end of the row, out in the open. Nancy made a run at them; Ginnie drove her back with a barrage of white roses. The battle, the sight, the sound, filled me with joy.

We were us again.

I slipped out from behind an urn and harvested the prized munitions; a hail of flower heads struck me. I could tell which ones my brother threw because they were thrown hard enough to hurt and they all hit my head. I shook moist petals out of my ears and smiled, ignoring the sting of hurtled buds against my cheek as I dropped the mums in the bucket I'd made from my skirt.

Suddenly the doors swung open and a white rectangle of light flashed from the hallway. "What the hell is this?" Uncle John's voice boomed.

He snapped on the light. I dropped my skirt full of mums. Petals covered the floor. Stripped flower stalks stuck out of the vases, looking raw and painful.

"Your father is lying dead in the next room and you're playing? Laughing? What's wrong with you kids?" he shouted, heartbroken, enraged.

"Uncle John," Ginnie said, always the brave one. I just stood and glowered, hating him with all my heart.

"Get OUT of here," he said. "Go stand by your mother." As we filed silently passed, Uncle John grabbed Gil's wrist. "Go on, girls," Uncle John said, holding Gil back. "Close the door."

Aunt Margo found us in the hallway trying to listen at the door and insisted we rejoin our mother at the side of the casket. A few minutes later Gil joined us there, red-eyed and pale. Ginnie glanced around for nearby adults and then I heard her whisper. "Uncle John's a…*jagoff.*"

The Fawn

Looking through the patio door of a friend's house on a crisp spring morning, Sylvie saw a fawn dash across the gray and oxblood flagstones. All ears and legs, white dots on sleek henna, the fawn was blank slate beauty. It carried the little flash of white on its rump and tail in unbearably tender bravado. No mother attended, and the baby, rattled, maybe even by Sylvie's silhouette, flung itself out of her line of sight.

It was followed immediately by an identical sibling who stumbled under a glass-topped table. With bated breath, Sylvie watched as it tried to navigate the cream colored metal supports. The fawn knuckled under with the hazards. Its nose crashed into the flagstones, the knots of its knees banging on obstructions. The door muffled all sound, but the fawn wasn't making any. Sylvie knew that deer don't cry when they're hurt. She called out to her friend, "Hurry. Come and see this beauty." She reached for the door handle and saw that her movement created panic in this tiny interloper, too.

It leaped up, trembling, and high stepped over the remaining bars. But then it stood still, tail tucked hard and sides heaving. Sylvie opened the door, thinking to somehow help and wondering what had stopped it. The father of her friend appeared, an old man with white hair wisping around his ears in the little breeze, a kind, toothy smile and large age-mottled hands. He knelt beside the tiny creature. His hand slid under its chest and he lifted it slightly toward himself, steadying. The fawn's legs splayed out stiffly. It didn't struggle.

"Don't worry, Little Girlie," he said quietly, "I'm going to save you." Sylvic exhaled, relaxing, relieved that someone knew what they were doing. Then she watched as he held the fawn carefully, placed his hand in its mouth and ripped out its tongue. "Now, you won't have any trouble," he said as he stood and dropped the tongue. He brushed his hand off on his pant leg. Together, they watched while the fawn staggered on its impossibly thin legs, head to the ground. The tongue made a last curl, a fat pink leaf lying alone on the flagstones. Dumbstruck and horrified, Sylvie looked up from the tongue toward her friend's father.

She woke with a gasp. First, she struggled to right the dream, to arrive at a different ending. Then she comforted herself, insisting it was only a dream. But that after-feeling of sorrow and horror lingered, that desire to make it right. Working again through the events, could she have saved it? And threading through her reminiscence was a niggling idea, an idea that the dream meant something.

Sylvie shifted under the heavy, inert arm of her husband, raised her head to look at the clock, and worried; did she want to go back to sleep and maybe dream that dream again?

Hospital Walks

slick dry channels
      turn left
turn right
      straight ahead
          turn again
Follow the green stripes on the floor.

donors honored medaled march
      above me alongside me
What did they give?

fake halls   worn trails
smooth oak tubular rails

flesh tone walls angled pores swollen
      with splotted flowers washed wiped
    paintings not real or surreal (they exist only here)
      sapped sunsets never seen seas
Follow the green stripes on the floor.

through above-ground tunnels
    past square sided holes
where daylight is denied entry
    and false lights lie inside

carrion blue cages white coats
    rush the chute
Follow the green stripes on the floor.

The Rocking Chair

She told me about the black tall-backed rocking chair.

Its long, spindled bars are spaced and curved
perfectly to not hurt when you lean back.

She said my grandfather brought the rocker when I was born.

The rocking chair's arms end
in tiny round fists that feel snug under your fingers.

Now pale stripes of bare wood peek out from the blackness.

She is here.

After Max Ernst's *Epiphany*

Faun, fauna, flora. Earth altar. All is algid in the green twilight. The bull is the central creature in this ceremony—deformed horn, the small eye, half-shut. A hoof reaches forward, as if to rise, stand, escape, but already his body has become a hillock. *Do you eat of this flesh.* The priest's language sounds like paper rattling. His curate, yellow-eyed, a face slate and nacreous, lets his needle-sharp teeth peek: an eager assent. There will be an eclipse tomorrow. During the wait for occultation, half the bull's face has turned to spores. The priest straddles the bull. Tomorrow the priest will open the bull with his hands. The bull will break like paper, like a cluster of dried bullwort. The priest will be standing in offal. It will be his first. A weak splash of blood will turn the surrounding trees rusty. From those trees will be born a new generation of priests.

Origin Story

I come from out of the teeth
of knaves. Skin and ink: chiaroscuro.

An idyll of spring,
a knot of knots, and not, not, not.

Coffee and spoon.
Moon-baying woman.

One with wistful fists, a gentle egg
ungentled. Scratchedout.

Birth defect, ornament,
troubling water.

Hiss and click and rattle,
sea turtle totem,
silent glide,
quiet plight.

A synonym for lack of light.

Barbs in the blood.
Garrulous. Amazing mess.
Libra rising.

Formula

I have found there is no straight line to the surface,
no borders to keep the hunger at bay when it crawls
into bed with me, no way to find a solution to infinity.

Still, I understand the equation.

I know the way my cells burst
when you pluck me from a field of lost, the way
you smooth my insecurities like white linen on hotel beds.

Most of all, I know the way
my spine contracts and collapses,
unraveling
me at the sight of you leaving.

Saved

They believed
there was a science
to the way it happened,
ash skin fading
fast to blue in the bathroom light.

My arms locked up,
rigid as the walls
separating left and right brain
unable to see with rolled back eyes
you, sweating there on the hemisphere.

They admired
how I hit the floor with such precision
What a flawless dance, and it was—
narrowly missing my cerebellum
limbs crumpled like tissue paper.

They were amazed
at the way my pulse played hide and seek
then how the flow of blood back into my brain
washed realization over you:
squeezing my hands,
kissing impossible breaths into my lungs,
compressing what you couldn't fathom in your hands.
A savior over science.

They said the tests were inconclusive—
It is unexplainable.
I said, *Put all your bets on theories*
Prove your faith in God
And they couldn't speak.

KARA KNICKERBOCKER

After the Emptied

The dream tulips' yellow matches
the yawn of sea fog—entering; each

beach burr bares thorn-strong spokes &
like the head—sticks to what it thinks.

I cut apple & watch
fog lick stems.

Snow Came Fast Today

I watch two pigeons swell their chests
and press purple and grey, belly to belly.
The need for heat drove them a few feet
from my attic window to a ledge
under my neighbor's roof.

I raise the stuck pane to aim my camera
through the screen's mesh. Patches
of frozen excrement don't matter.
They tuck beaks and balloon bellies
to larger than pregnant.

The need to press
and keep—
heat from falling.

Grievances

My father's mind a fitful tape recorder
　that seizes and plays
　　a well-worn track of grievances:

the interviewer at a bank
　fifty years ago
　　who pushed to find out

whether he was Catholic,
　and so, not good enough to hire.
　　A friend, long dead,

who didn't phone him years before
　to see how he was after an operation.
　　My brother and I

who didn't side with him
　when our mother left him
　　for another man.

My father sits by the empty hearth,
　stranded in his chair
　　from which he cannot move

without help.
　He watches me as we talk.
　　I am caught in my own, unspoken—

being five or six
　sitting on the sofa with him
　　one Christmas

when he showed me how to use
   a cassette recorder, recited
      good fences make good neighbors

and then held the microphone
   to my lips.
      I stuttered a few words

and he shook his head and left.

MICHELLE MAHER

Collision

our child-nimble fingers snatch *onesies twosies*
catch the red ball *carts-before-horses* scoop up jacks
flip our palms in syncopated summer rhythm
the painted porch glossy grey-blue cool
under bare knees
three-for-three we stretch out on stomachs
grasp points between thumbs and forefingers
set the steel stars spinning
one-by-one straight-spine ballerinas
pirouette in place until the imperfect surface takes its toll
wobbling ever so slightly but still spinning
spiraling in mad circles wonderfully wildly out of control
ten ever-widening trajectories destined to cross
we watch mesmerized awaiting the inevitable

A Slow Grief

I'm not an adult.

It's not true, but it feels closer to reality than the truth. It's been years since Ana walked across the stage at college graduation, even longer since she shook the hand of her high school principal and rode home in the backseat of her parents' car, Declan beside her. He was barely fourteen years old then, and brimming with impatience to be home.

She thinks of him and drums her fingers on the steering wheel of her car, staring with the same annoyance at the brake lights ahead of her. She gets home from work and sits by the window of her fifth floor apartment, leaning her head on the glass and listening absently. Several times an hour, the city bus aggressively leaves the stop a block down, and the sound, like a toy truck, makes her forget all the other sounds—all the sirens, car horns, pedestrians yelling across the street. Her cat jumps into her lap and watches birds fitfully landing in the tree by the front door, his eyes wide and focused and alive.

Lucky bastard.

She wants to get up, to change out of her scratchy work pants that don't fit, yank off her pantyhose, make some tea. She wants to see her fiancé, feel his touch, be held and kissed and made love to. But she doesn't move. Another bus departs on the street below, and already the sound is stuck between her ears. She closes her eyes and sees a Tonka dump-truck, the kind with a big red button on the top. Over and over, Declan used to push the truck through the hall outside his bedroom, and the sound, like a city bus, reached her even through closed doors. She wants it to stop. As the light fades outside, her apartment darkens, tempting her to close her eyes and rest. But she doesn't sleep. Her body is exhausted, her mind beyond comprehensible thought, but she doesn't sleep. Her cat jumps down to the floor and stares at her, meows, cries for food. She remembers her own hunger, but no longer feels it.

The next day at work, she sits at her desk and the sun is in her eyes. She thinks about pulling a blanket over her face, about sinking into bed and doing nothing. She closes her eyes and sees Declan riding his bike around their old neighborhood. There is glee on his face, unrelenting joy, because he is riding without his training wheels. He was a big kid, one of the clan, not a little brother. Never again a *little* brother. Now he could go camping with them, in real woods, not their backyard. She thinks of the trails and the rocks and dirt; she thinks of the trees and the sun. She can almost feel the grit in her socks, damp from walking through creeks and puddles, following Declan as he carved his way through his first camping trip. She remembers their father pitching the tent, Declan sitting by the fire, his legs slack and exhausted, the resilience on his face, pure determination not to look too tired, too worn out to be bigger and older now.

Ana makes herself look at her computer, check her email. She has reports to generate, grants to edit. Her boss approaches and asks about her day, and how are things, anyway? She smiles, but nothing feels different.

No part of me is okay.

Later she sees her fiancé for dinner. They go to a nice restaurant and dress in nice clothes. He thinks this will help, the flavors, the cocktails, the dim ambiance. Her parents never took her and Declan to places like this. Too expensive, too exotic. She wonders if he'd even like it here, with the industrial steel rafters and barn wood floors, the bacon-wrapped dates and shishito peppers in olive oil, aged scotch and Peychaud's Bitters. She rubs her lips together, feeling the luxury of added color, of crimson, and dabs her napkin along her mouth. She touches the imprint with her thumb, the color, like blood, appearing much darker in the low light. Before she can stop it, her mind envisions what he must have looked like, clothes torn, the car mangled, everything becoming more and more red. More and more crimson.

The waiter comes by and asks if they'd like dessert, but all she can do is shake her head, as if the motion will banish more than just the inquiry. As if it will *make it stop*.

At home, she heads to the bathroom, turns on the water and lets it run, listening to the sound of the drain as her eyes close. She sees him again, but he's taller now. He's shaved his head to look more like their father, and as she listens, she hears his childhood laugh turn into the deep voice of his manhood, how she sometimes mistook him for their father when she would call home. She wonders how long it will be before she forgets what he sounds like, before the nuance of his character is lost to the passage of time and the dissipation of grief.

Abruptly she turns the water off and banishes the lingering echo of it in her ears, clinging instead to his voice, what he sounded like when he'd say, quickly and with childish shame, that he'd missed her when she moved away.

She goes to bed and balls the blanket in her fist. She squeezes her eyes shut and sees him, young, growing up, a picture beside a casket. It wasn't long after she'd left their small town that he'd left them all for good. Tiny droplets dampen her pillow, and soon she feels her fiancé's arm around her middle, a kiss on her back. He squeezes her and she knows he knows, and she smiles despite the pressure swelling around her lungs.

"I love you," she says.

And in the broken silence, as if in unison, "I love you, too."

Honeydew

the fruit of my childhood. Not the peach from the Beaver County farm,
where Kayleigh took a bite and a pincher bug crawled out. Not the apple
painted with peanut butter from preschool, nor the strawberries
that crept through the fence from Gerace's yard. It's the honeydew that Mom
bought from Weis's, stickered with a farm name from Arizona.
We'd choose based on scent, whether the sweetness from the stem tickled our noses.
Sometimes we were duped—the flesh more green than white.
When it was just right, the melon melted in my fingers.
This was an August tradition.

Today, I carve honeydew shipped from Guatemala.
The cutting boards are in the dishwasher, but the knife is sharpened.
I paper towel the counter while my husband naps. I am 32,
the sun is hot. I wonder why Mom never gardened.
I have tried for years on our apartment's balcony—too much sun, too little.
I want this melon to be perfect, to satisfy my loneliness, the anxiety
felt when I wake to the alarm clock's indigo light in the middle of the night.
Some things must grow full.
I cut through the center—such a ceremony.
This one isn't ripe. I scoop the seeds into the garbage disposal.
Cut the honeydew into rectangles. Refrigerate it for later.

Labor

Even though it was just 15 minutes,
the walk to work along Fifth Avenue seemed so much longer
than the walk home.

Maybe it's the way anyone feels on the way to work.
On the way to a small classroom, where children eat,
paint flowers with little, fat fingers, sing *Do you know the muffin man?*

I look at them and think, *It's amazing how quickly you become the same.*
How each of them falls flat when they first try to run. They whimper
when Mommy leaves, put books in their mouths, shriek over anything.

That winter I read *The Yellow Wallpaper.* How it resonated with me.
I felt trapped in that classroom. The walls were indeed yellow.
The children so needy I once said, *Perhaps I'll lie down.*

You can just walk on top of me. I couldn't quit.
There was rent and bills to pay. The one time, I cursed the sun
as it blinded me during the walk home in mid-February.

I was enraged over an indulgent parent who watched her son
kick another child in the head. *Toddlers*, she shrugged.
Such an ass and the son paid for her inanity.

On that walk, I stopped to wipe some dead skin from my glasses when
the frames cracked in half. The cold, I guessed. Or, was it karma, an omen
that the walk both ways would always ache.

TERESA NAREY

Cat Walk

Birds whirl and scream
outside my window—
the summer day immersed
in sun and breath.

Next door the cat slides
under low slung branches
to retrieve a fallen chick.
A moment later

I glimpse the cat gliding
in a slow whisper past
my yard. I cannot see
its guarded face.

The birds are quiet now.

Thank you, but

I don't want to talk about lockdowns
of the heart or planetary speculations
or how pit bulls, if treated well,

can be trustworthy. I prefer instead
to concentrate on tiny hummingbirds
who fly vast distances to gather

rare nectars in order to survive;
how their varicolored feathers—
blues and greens—or ruby throats

gleam in the sun attracting mates
or frightening rivals. How fiercely
they fight for territory—and lovers.

MARILYN MARSH NOLL

After a Day of Fitful Rain

that has broken the heat of August,
I watch from across the street.
A thick bunch of thin wild grasses
at the edge of the alley and a flock
of sparrows on the sidewalk.

Every few seconds one flies up,
perches for a second on a strand of grass,
which bends to the ground
and the other sparrows furiously
eat the seeds. It happens over

and over, not clear to me
whether it's the same bird
weighting down the grass
or several birds taking turns.

Full Moon on Christmas Eve, 2015

It's supposed to happen only every 19 years,
but the full, luminous moon on Christmas Eve
was the first for forty years. It hung there

in the dark sky, seemed so close you could almost
touch its surface, man on the moon, slumped against
its round edges as if tired of his job.

I'd never seen this December 24th full moon before.
It somehow signified that we ought to think
of something grand, quiet and shared.

LIANE ELLISON NORMAN

Helen's Photograph

In the photograph my eyes roll up
to branches centrifuging out
testament to the swing force
of open air love.

Spring of '37, low stone wall
dirt schoolyard, leaning back into his arms
and the slant of the earth,
commencement just an incantation
on the principal's fat wet lips.

A hand through dark curls,
a whisper to my neck,
crinkle of perfumed handkerchief
tucked deep in my brasserie.

Will he be back soon? And alive?
Sick from too much whiskey?
The letter: frozen toes and same socks
for three months. A strange bright
stamp, hemlock green.

I need to   I should

sparrow thoughts scatter off
          to better crumbs

Whose old lady
hands are these,
picking, jabbing, piercing
under liver brown spots,
under calcified nails,
for the buried thread of memory
left deep in the flesh?

Defining Color

Can I define color?
Bring myself to this black white and indigo task?

Am I the deliverer of the message you need to receive?
How color can be so thin it rips like tissue paper? A sea

of blue-green wavelengths—eyes so bright they take over my brown,
leave me feeling ghost-white like paper.

Can skin be white like college-ruled or whiteout kept in a bottle so small?
Give me the color purple, fresh grape juice

dark and dripping blood. I hate yellow and green
undertones my skin carries. I am jaundiced,

like a liver poisoned, the something wrong. I want to feel
the glorious color of brown, a deep and sandy sienna.

I long for the deepness of a tan so I watch my skin burn,
crisp reds in this tanning bed, hoping I can turn into some better skins.

Henry Pina

When my Grandfather was born in 1917,
in New Bedford, MA, the soft subtle tones
in his skin did not evoke *colored*,

and the label inked in heavy black
on his birth certificate was *white*.
In 1962, he went to the Federal office

to make a quick color change,
but the paperwork was thick
and the pale blonde behind the counter

said it was a *beneficial oversight*.
The tattered paper is off-white
and yellowing, its color deepening

through the years, but the *white*
never fades. He tries to rub off
the black ink with the brown edges

of his creased fingertips, spirals
swirling in the prints of his thumbs,
but it won't come off.

Weekend Turkey Kill

In Western Pennsylvania sons join fathers,
uncles, brothers, neighbors in the hunt.
Sportsmen, released from school, office
or the end of construction season,
drive pickups to forested cabins
along the Allegheny River.

Men outfitted in camouflage compete
for the first shot. A local woodsman,
in cap and red plaid jacket, his rifle ready,
tracks through dried leaves with his
sniffing hound. The lone hunter spots
a solitary bird soaring free, free
like himself on Saturday.

Through November's mottled clouds,
a rifle shot strikes the wild turkey.
The lone hunter scores, his hound bolts,
the prey grounded by gravity.
The hunter inspects his kill: speckled
brown feathers shroud sweet fowl
meat, a trophy trussed, bagged,
ready for the chef's knife.

ANNE PICONE

The Boys Outside

Gabriel sucked energy from the *quadra* below, its pink satin walls seeming to split at the seams from the one hundred and fifty drummers, six thousand voices and twelve thousand feet given over to the Saturday night samba. The sound was enough to snatch from the sky the drone of approaching traffic and the roar and whoosh as it passed. Yet the air stirred with vibrations deeper than the fleeting undertow of the high-sided vans, yellow taxis, and bone-shaking trucks. The vibrations of the ancestors, his mother called it, may she rest in peace.

He turned to Bernard, whose lips were glued, as usual, to a can of Guarana. He drank more of that stuff than any boy in Rio, Gabriel was sure. Couldn't last ten minutes without its sweet rush. Gabriel didn't need it, it wasn't even midnight, but he wanted to sugarcoat the taste of car exhaust in his mouth. He touched shoulders with his friend and hovered his finger over the Guarana berries on the can and, grudgingly, Bernard handed it over.

The chorus rose up to their perch on the overpass, high in the concrete amphitheater at the heart of the Mangueira district. *Mangueira*. Mango tree, ripe with fruit. From where his legs dangled over the street party that sprang from the roots of the Samba School's headquarters, Gabriel could reach even *this* fruit on the topmost branches. He ate from it slowly, first running his lips over the familiar shape of the tune, humming, then breaking off words he couldn't help but know, shyly, with those embarrassing teeth of his, until the juice of the melody flooded his small body and he sang at the top of his lungs, not even hearing his own voice—let alone Bernard's—floating up the hillside with the vapor of the vendors' rice, waiting, waiting for the drums to take him. The voices stopped. Four beats of traffic masked the samba *virada*, its turn, and Bernard sailing beside him. Then the machine-gun-fire of the *tamborims*, loud enough to put the fear of God in the hearts of the neighboring Vila Isabel supporters. Gabriel smiled at the thought, and at the rocking tick-tock of the hand-drums moving back and forth, keeping that swing in the Mangueira march, until, that was, his half-grown ears picked out a strangulation at the end of their last phrase, the sound of a mistake and attempted cover-up.

"Tamborim section fucked up!" Gabriel squeaked. The clatter of two dozen shakers, their hundreds of metal discs reverberating, drowned him out. He shot Bernard a look, expecting to see his own feelings on the matter reflected back. But his friend's head was buried in his hands; his body wriggling under clamped arms. Pitiful. Far more so than the slip-up, even if it was only three weeks to Carnival and Mangueira hadn't won since the year before the two were born.

Gabriel brushed the bare blubber of Bernard's back, unearthed one of his ears and cupped a hand around it. "Come on, man, it wasn't Dani." Without uncoiling, Bernard swatted at him half-heartedly, the way poor children bat at flies when they remember to. Just pitiful.

Bernard's cousin, Dani, was the youngest drummer in Mangueira, a matter of family pride, born with a *tamborim* in his hands. Dani was inside the *quadra* now, in the gallery, second row back, fourth person in, below the Sacred Heart of Jesus, watching little Beatriz shake what she had—her thirteen, so she didn't have much—and waiting for the Guarana, or beer, if the master wasn't looking, to come his way.

Gabriel looked at his lap to find he was cracking his fingers. He moved them to rest on the warm concrete and felt Bernard uncoil beside him. Good. If he listened now he'd hear his precious cousin play cleanly. Or rather, he'd hear only the clockwork of the *tamborim* machinery inside the Mangueira train. Gabriel wasn't even aware he was tapping it out until his fingers stopped, mid-measure, at the soda can to his left. It was still cool. He glanced at his friend. Bernard's hands were pressed together in his lap, and he stared at the green letters that spanned the *quadra's* facade, looking constipated. Was he getting an Adam's apple or just a fat neck from too much sugar? Gabriel took a long drink of the Guarana.

"Hey!" Bernard's wet fingers groped at him. "I already gave you some. Dani gave it to me." *Meu Deus*, Dani again. Dani the big fish with all the soda but not a *real* to his name. Gabriel gulped down what was left, shook the can in front of Bernard, and offered it to him.

"Dani can get you another one. Didn't he tell you they had crates of it stacked inside?"

A giant truck screamed past so Gabriel didn't have to listen to Bernard's protests. He just watched them, like TV with the volume turned down. Poor boy. If Dani really gave a shit about him, why didn't he get his cousin a free pass inside the *quadra*? Bernard's black hair stood up in a goodbye wave to the truck, like in a cartoon. He pounded the can with his fist and tossed it down on the others who didn't have the twenty *real* to get inside. What if he hit one of their neighbors? A *Carapau de corrida*, he imagined his mum saying. A racing mackerel, trying to get ahead. Bernard wasn't finished, but a little of the venom had drained from his face.

"You're just jealous, Buckteeth!" Bernard took a deep breath, satisfied with the insult. The *tamborims* and shakers also paused. The quiet turn of the samba. The time to get reverential about the song. Not its lyrics, because only the judging panel cared about them, but its *feeling*. Gabriel pictured Beatriz blowing a strand of loose hair from her face, radiant with effort, sparkling in Mangueira pink and green up in the gallery above the stage, her back to the drums.

"Beatriz would rather have my buckteeth than your fat ass!"

Bernard teetered on the edge for a few seconds, then fell on the funny side. Even his weight on Gabriel's shoulder couldn't stop it from shaking, they both laughed so hard. The idea that Miss Junior Queen of the Drums would be seen dead with either of them. Or even see them, the boys outside.

Memoir

After Mihaela Moscaliuc

Pema Chodron says *Love of the truth puts you on the spot.*
Thirty years later I recognized a face in a newspaper.
The story of rape is the story of traumatic forgetting.
If I told you that story now, I would choke on *Coral Watts.*
Article wadded into a drawer. Mind gone blank. Flinching
at right-shouldered touch, making love, I fight
to stay in my body. I thought he had a knife.
I thought I smelled pot. I hadn't understood why
I begged for my life. Daughter of a racist,
I believed I was collateral damage,
not the near-victim of a serial killer.
Once I became a guinea pig at University Hospital.
Doctors thought me psoriatic, provided ointments.
When two interns tried to burn me with acid, I fled.
Once I tried to mend a married, lecherous man
so he would love me right, but gave up. A narcissist
like my father. Just different politics and smarter.
More than once, I have been passed over. Twice,
I tripped, first over luggage, then a curb. Sprawling
across tile and pavement, bruises blackened up and
hurt so much I could barely see I had been given grace.

LAURA J. ROOP

The Present Moment

A few days above fifty degrees,
and already I'm shoveling compost,
enlarging the flower bed for planting.
Disturbed earthworms dangle and curl
back into cut turf. I'm overeager,
and these new roses might pay.

Two stolid bushes in peat pots.
Hearty-looking. Not lovely yet, but
I can envision Peace roses spiraling up
thorny canes along the deck. And Japanese
irises filling the low spot near the well, and
lilies of the valley. Cardinal flowers. Bee balm.

The weather has hardly broken. It could
snow tomorrow, and already I'm picturing
a summer without bee stings, without
unfulfilled promise. As a child, I wished away
the present moment, believing life didn't really
begin until I lived in a woman's body.

I imagined my childhood falling away
like a broken chrysalis. No loss in that loss.
I never dreamed body and spirit alike
could break but revive, pain spaded
so deep it couldn't be smoothed, so deep
it would shape everything after.

So I'm learning to mix humus with sand,
to be patient with imperfect earth,
to cradle a plant's roots in my hands
as I ease it toward its new home. To bless it,
bulb, blossom, and thorn.
Love the broken leaf.

Do Not Desert Me, Places I Have Loved

My body cleaves to life
like iron shavings to a magnet.
I've left you, Lake Minnetonka,
Mt. Rainier, Cape Flattery—each,

a magnetic north. Cleft from you
I fall weightless, a rock of aging.
Cleft from you I lose my way.
Places I have loved—Nisqually Valley,

Gifford Pinchot Forest, Rock Lake.
A vial of Pacific Ocean sand tucked
six decades in a dresser drawer.
Burnished inner bark hung

on the living room wall. Shells
from Neah Bay, river rock from
Lake Michigan—my weft
across the weaving years.

SUSAN SHAW SAILER

I haunt the edges of my past,

prowl for nicks and wrinkles. This chip
presents the morning, slick with being
twelve, I hurt my mother, certain
I was in the zone. This crease recalls
the day when, first home from college,
I told granddad there was no god,
nothing sacred. Craving certainty
I found none, undertow dissolving
sand beneath my feet. Slack in
confidence, taut with promise, I sought
sieves to separate my chaff from wheat.
Though I danced with light, I knew
the darkness in a stone.

The Music Room at Niagara on The Lake

My husband drifts off to sleep.
Tomorrow, forty-three years of marriage.
Tonight, I'll imagine making love
to the music of Rosina Wachtmeister.
Her painting, *Composition for Piano and Cello*
hangs on the wall opposite our bed.
Cello and music sheets ready.
Where is the piano? Where is the musician?

My husband lies snoring on the left side
of our anniversary bed beside Rosina's
other painting of piano, music sheets
and an empty piano bench. Where is the pianist?
A violin hangs on my side of our anniversary bed,
Where is the bow? Where is the music

in this burgundy room of roses—roses
on the door, roses on the violin, roses
on the bed sheets, roses on the quilt
of our anniversary bed. Where is the musician?

What You Must Never Forget

You must never forget your first trolley ride,
how you sat in the back next to your mother
convinced the bearded man in front
reading a newspaper and picking his teeth
was out to get you, would take you away.
That was the first time you sensed danger
although you were too young to name it.
You sensed it the way a baby wren senses
when he is about to be captured, the way
you sensed it that day in the grocery store
when you began sorting the multicolored coupons
while you waited for your mother at the checkout counter
until your hand slipped and a rainbow
of colors scattered at your feet.
It was danger that made you run
out of the store without your mother,
run as fast as you could home
to your father sitting barefoot on your porch swing,
string in hand, ready to pull
the upright shoe box over a baby wren.

Cracks

My father cracks an egg with the edge of a spoon and dumps
the globe and ooze into a tin bowl. Whips it up with a fork,
pours a puddle of oil onto the hot skillet and spills the froth
into the center. It blooms out, a dull chrysanthemum.

He is making breakfast for my niece. Her granddad's eggs
are the only eggs she will eat anymore, with fried brown edges
that crunch between her two-year molars. As she eats, he sits
softly with her and dabs a napkin to her lips.

When I was a girl, my father cracked me like an egg. Whacked
me good with wooden words or his spoon of silence. I never
bloomed big and bright until my father was an old man. Now,
his anger is a mum-shaped shadow of memory.

Rita Uses a Condom

the purple one felt like a garbage bag / *I mean it's not even valid enough*
to be real sex / the October we all started using condoms again /
how much do they even cost / haven't paid for them since 2007 /
frowning / oh, how latex stretches /
the "how to use a condom" handbook /
even in Spanish /
didn't help

Somebody lost her weave last night

and it blends in with the brown leaves on the ground.
This abandon makes me happy
and I wonder if she misses it
and when she noticed it missing
and maybe she feels lighter.

Yesterday I started a letter to you:
Dear Steve, what do you think of David Lynch movies?
I collect notes, little things I want to tell you, but don't
because I like you and don't want you to think I'm crazy.
Like:
Do you think Conor Oberst is a sell out?
I'm envious of the hummingbird,
its 3,900 mile migratory pattern from Mexico to Alaska.
How do you really feel about tacos?

Would you still like me if you knew
there are days I wear sadness like a black party dress
and this morning in the shower I found a bruise on my breast
from some guy the other night. I can't remember his name.
I can't remember the last time I touched something and really felt it.
At work people come up to me and want things:
help with term papers, to know where the printer is
and sometimes I can't remember their faces, but they know me.
I worry I'll never be able to give them what they need.

This morning I'm walking to the bus stop on 18th
thinking about egg sandwiches,
vending machine coffee,
love letters I'm too afraid to send.

KAYLA SARGESON

My Benton Street

I

I know I cannot go, though it's not far.
Isn't that the point—it was so small.
I would not ask, not come to feed some more
From that worn air, those dim, those clouded skies,
Or that soft road, that sigh, whose fall, whose rise
Whose heft lives deep in me.

II

The blue is a weed but not in that time of falling
Through air. Not when the beech leaves were melting to mud,
The bruised veinous hook-handed skunk cabbage hinted and grunted
And snigged at us, smeared in our bog. What shove of ice
What blink and what toggle suggested, imagined that warm lick
Of tar, and that fall? It's so small. That soft road, that sigh
Whose rise is mapped in me.

III

                              There is nothing here
That could make you weep except waiting for the lights
To speak to us. And King—we pray
To that one-eared dog to sleep with his wound turned away
While we eat. Mrs. Ambler—you go. Go with your cats
And do not tell what you know. We'll pretend it's your fault
That you're old and they smell. Let go. We'll hoard
The rest, the rising. It's in us. Barely feel
The completeness it offers, its lift, entire, the sureness
Of arms, inescapable depth. In my core I breathe
My street, it breathes with me no matter where
I am. Oh soft and sweet, the curves of a body
I know. I cannot go down to that turn in my road.

An excerpt from a novel-in-progress,
A Place on Laurel Run

"What do you think of the fish Daniel's got at his place, Aralee?" John asked her.

Nate spoke up before she could answer. "The thing is, you have to be careful to call it the fish-er-ee." He checked for reactions among his brothers who sat with them around the farm table. Thomas gave Nate a sharp jab of approval, and the others laughed.

"Now, boys," Cate warned. Her mouth tugged downward, and from what Aralee knew of her, Cate's tone seemed unnatural. Her sons ignored her.

Aralee took a biscuit from a shallow tray nearby. She had to reach what seemed an impolite distance and hoped they'd take her lapse of etiquette as a stranger among them as a sign of her feeling at home. "I was very impressed by Daniel's knowledge and what he's done. The fish, and so many of them, seem to be thriving." She focused on buttering her biscuit and ignored the not-so-muted snickers from Daniel's three brothers.

"How many fishes has he got over there now?" Thomas spoke for the first time since Aralee's arrival.

"Not enough to make a living," snorted John. "Trout Boy's got a long way to go to make it."

"And that suits you just fine, doesn't it? Then you could frack all day and night and not give a damn who gets hurt." Daniel exploded, his face red, his jaw working.

"The natural gas to operate this place alone would be a windfall, not to mention royalties," John said, leaning far into the table to edge his angry face closer to Daniel's across from him. "We'd make more money in a year from one well than you'd make in a lifetime raising fish." He spat the words out. Daniel leaned in too, ready to unload, but his father interrupted.

"I won't have this!" Cam slammed his open hand on the table. "And I mean it."

Silence fell. John's face reddened. Little Bud, John's toddler, pouted and tears welled in his wide eyes. Cate's mouth opened and closed like the gasping trout Aralee had seen earlier.

"Don't count your chickens, John." Cam's words were controlled and the hand that had struck the table now lay flat but tensed. He scowled at his son. "And Daniel, you better get used to the fact that you're part of this family and the family business. You owe us that."

Aralee sensed he wanted to say more. He turned to her instead.

"You'll have to excuse the boys here." Cam's voice was calm, but the threat remained thick at the table and in his tight jaw that skewed his smile.

"It's okay, Cam. I grew up with brothers." She smiled but felt as intimidated as Little Bud.

"Aralee is going to help with the design of the stained glass window at church," Cate said as sullen uneasiness settled over her husband, sons, and two of their wives.

"Watch out, Aralee, she'll have you up to your eyeballs with helping." Nate's wife Kim gave Aralee a wink, either oblivious to the tension or wanting to break it.

Cam smiled, too. "That's good," he said as he pushed a last bite of beans onto his fork with a biscuit. Aralee wondered if he even realized what Cate or Kim had said.

At the back door, pairs of heavy work boots were lined up, each well-worn and muddy. John rose from the table first and strode to them in white-socked feet. As he passed Daniel, he ran a hand over his hair, and Daniel glowered. John grabbed his boots and pulled them on. "I'll see you boys out in the field." He started out the door then half turned and called out. "Nice meeting you, Aralee. Stop back. Maybe you can deck out this old place." He seemed less heated, but a scowl played at the edges of his mouth.

Cam nodded at his oldest son but directed his comment to Aralee. "I don't see there's much room for improvement with the decor. What do you think?"

Aralee, wanting to appear unaffected and bright, followed Cam's gaze that scanned the dated and grease-stained kitchen cabinets. She thought the room shabby, but in a well-used and loved way, certain that many happier meals had occurred here. "Maybe just a little," she said.

He laughed, and Aralee looked at Cate whose crinkled smile barely clothed her distress.

Amid taunts and jibes, the other brothers scraped back their chairs, each rising to pull on his own work boots. With goodbyes, they trudged out to their waiting chores. Aralee looked at the kitchen clock that hung above the faux copper range hood. One o'clock. It seemed the entire afternoon had passed in a brief hour.

Kim and Cate began to clear the dishes and attend to Bud. In the scurry of departures, Cate spoke up. "Daniel, dear, use your dad's truck and take Aralee home."

"I'll do it," Cam said but hadn't moved from his chair at the head of the table. He stared at his youngest son. "You help Nate on the east slope."

Aralee turned to see Daniel's stormy face. Their eyes locked for a moment, then he ducked his head. When he raised it again, he had a lost look, all boy. She felt smothered at being inexorably pulled into the affairs of this boisterous family, like it or not. And she had no one to blame but herself. She had known Daniel only briefly but felt an inexplicable and fierce compulsion to defend him and his dream. And she wanted to be a friend to Cate, too.

Cam had his eyes on her, but she stood and called out to Daniel. "Thank you for the tour today. I enjoyed seeing your trout ponds."

Daniel looked back at her with a weak smile. "Thanks," he muttered, then left. The back door closed softly behind him.

Pauline
1915-1998

a contradiction of wisdom and uncertainty
having done as she should all her life
orphaned by all she holds dear
no one to take care of her
no one to take care of
no one to take care
no one to care
no one

Painted.

O God, more than my imagination…

When I die, will I have hands that move, hands that will hold a paint brush?

The names of things will rest on my tongue. I'll have to lick the canvas.

Planning the Reunion

There is the boy who killed himself:
easy to locate, a backcountry road at dawn,
suicides never move away.
You remember the time behind the tennis courts,
his brother's hand played with your breast.
"I like girls who are different," he says,
and you smile past him, don't move away.
You don't care if he likes you or not.
You are thinking about his brother then,
wondering if he would have liked to touch your breast;
if any touch could have made a difference,
any need, any request.

Hold A Gun

While looking for family,
I found hollow tree trunks
filled with sugar, lard,

blood pudding, pig's feet.
I found cold hearts, rancid whiskey,
biting tongues, acid reflux.

I found hollow eyes,
laceration:
hands that could not help—

only slap,
push,
hold a gun.

M.A. SINNHUBER

Kind Man

He brushes her long hair,
uplifting strokes, pressing

her head to his chest.
Morning begins.

Jade gems. Apple slices.
Cheerful voices on the floor.

Soft as toast warming,
he holds her.

The sunny haze becomes critical
in the eyes of the patients on 5-D.

Once the morning smiles are dispensed,
the truth comes out.

I am afraid, she says,
to sleep on my back.

Christmas Break

I can feel his little slanted eyes watching. His movements, his speech, are slow and cautious so not to disturb me. His eyes close while he struggles for his words. Little Lindsay holds onto his vowels as if they won't let go of his tongue.

"What are you doing that for?"

"So I can make you some breakfast." I answer him without looking up.

"Are you making breakfast for everybody?"

"Yes I am, Baby."

I'm doing old school breakfast, everything from scratch. I stop peeling the potatoes but still stare at my hands, looking at the milky potato juice all over my milk chocolate-colored hands. They look like old lady hands. Hell, I am an old lady. Am I not talking to my 3-year-old great-grandson? I notice L.L. looking too. I've only been here one day and one overnight. He is still checking to see if I am friend or foe.

L.L. continued: "When my mom gets home, she can have something to eat? Will you make enough?"

"I sure will baby."

"Why are you so nice to us?"

"I love you all is why."

"You love us?" he said, tilting his head to get a better look at me.

"With all my heart."

He smiles and moves in, asking a regular little boy question now.

"Can I have a piece of that bacon?"

"Yes you can."

He manages to grab a piece of bacon and quickly put most of it into his mouth as if someone would take it from him. "This is good, MeMa."

The look of pleasure on his tiny face lights the room and lifts my heart. After a few moments, L.L. now has a different mission.

"Can I help make breakfast?"

"Sure, baby. Could you throw this stuff into the garbage for me?"

He nods. His tiny, strong hands reach up, take the plastic bag of potato skins and toss it into the kitchen trashcan. He is back in front of me in seconds. "Can I help cut those things?"

"The potatoes, no, baby, the knife is too sharp. You can help me rinse them in the sink."

He runs to get the stool and drags it across the kitchen floor to the sink. He's flashing the most downright blissful smile I've seen in years.

"I'm ready!" He's doing his back-and-forth head dance while I walk over to him with the bowl of potatoes. I turn on the faucet and pour out the dirty water, rinsing the juice from my hands. L.L. is enthusiastically awaiting his instruction.

"MeMa, I like helping."

"I can tell, thank you baby."

More little people footsteps and another small voice. It's 7-year-old Gabby. She has lost one of her two front teeth and it has grown in bigger than the rest. She is smiling, already scheming. She had been standing on the steps listening. "Could I have a bacon too, MeMa?"

"Absolutely, little lady."

She runs, grabs, then into the living room, shoving two pieces at once into her mouth. She turns quickly to see if I noticed.

"Gabby, you don't have to sneak, I said yes, and please don't shove food into your mouth like that."

Trying to chew, swallow, and talk at the same time, she choked out the words, "Okay MeMa, but I wasn't sneaking, Lindsay was trying to take all the bacon."

"Gabby, he was not, he's at the sink."

"But he's always taking stuff from me."

"I do not, Gabby." L.L. is clearly agitated and he starts to cry. Not just cry; wail would be the better word. I mean loud, like someone drew blood.

Now comes Big Lindsay shouting. "Boy, why are you making all that noise? Gabby, what did you do?"

"Nothing. I was just trying to…" Her voice is elevated; her eyes are wide and wild.

L.L. crying out, "She was saying stuff to me."

My grandson looks at me for clarification. I don't know why Gabby lied, why L.L. cried. I want to run out the house, but I am here in Georgia on Christmas vacation. All three are screaming, trying to be heard, but nobody is listening.

SYLVIA J. SMITH

An excerpt from a novel-in-progress, *Selection*

They line us up on the sweltering airfield. I stand proudly, tapping my foot to draw their attention. My narrow thigh widens at the barb of my knee, and my tendons tense magnificently down the inside of my leg. Standing in a circle while the scale is calibrated, they pretend that we can't see them. But I manage to catch the eye of one of the three suits. I smile and wink at him.

I reach over Iona and poke Paz in the rib. "Stand up straight. Doug is watching."

She stiffens, nervous. Her ass looks great in her tight, black briefs. We will have no problem getting onto the rocket.

Sweat is pouring from me although I haven't had anything to drink for two days. I rub my hands in anticipation. And to keep burning calories. Every ounce counts.

Line position was predetermined by our test scores. I flubbed the strength test, but I won't be doing any space walks. I'm an ace pilot, plus I'm the smallest. There's no way I'm not making it to launch.

They wave the first girl up, and she steps onto the scale. The bell clangs three times: She's been accepted. Ahead of me in line, Paz looks like she might retch. We've taken to curling up together at night. She's bigger than me, but even so I spoon myself around her cruel body and jam my tiny breasts into her back. It's all pretty innocent, but maybe once we're in space things will be different.

Next girl, same bell. Three clangs. Shit. I smolder in the desert heat at the middle of the line.

"All right, ladies!" Doug claps his fat, hairy hands together a few times, even though everyone's eyes were glued to him as soon as he stepped forward. "This is it. Remember, we only take FOUR."

He turns back as the next girl is helped onto the scale. She almost topples. Once she's on the scale, she can't even stand. One long buzz: disqualified.

Paz is up. She steps onto the platform, her long, dark hair swarming around her. Most girls have cut their hair to shed weight, but Paz won't. The scale climbs as her body stills. The bell rings three times! She jumps down and high-fives Doug, then runs off toward the cafeteria. Time for a feast, like we planned, except she's not waiting for me. She must be starving.

Next is Iona, whose legs shake as approaches the platform. The scale soars as she steadies. Then the bell rings three times, and Doug walks back out.

"Okay! We've got our crew. Best load yet—you'll eat in a year what took the last crew nine months. The accountants will love us." He keeps walking toward us, shooing us with his thick hands as if we were angry bees. "Now go get something to eat. Get outta here."

I slump over in the heat. I collapse right there on the flight line, and all the other girls walk by me, not caring. My skin blisters against the searing concrete.

"C'mon, Martinez," says Doug, toeing me softly in the gut with his leather loafer. "She'll be back in a year. Let's go get a burger."

In Town

someone buys a loaf of bread, another changes a tire.
The sun through the nursing home window
backlights death.

I hold Father's chilled hand/he doesn't hold mine—
he asks Mother, feet swollen in Sunday shoes, "Where's Robert?"

I search my jacket pockets—used tissues, crumbs,
pull out a quarter and my cell phone, call my brother
three states away, who flings himself into his car, already too late.

Silence lies with my short-breathed father in his bed.
Mother sits with them both, leans in to murmur, *Let go. It's ok.*

A red bi-plane bumps down an empty field.
Mother, her hair marcelled and shiny, shouts,
"Not yet! I'm not ready," clings
to a wood-and-wire fence.

O. mykiss

My father wasn't really dead.

Then he was. Then he wasn't.
Now he is. It took three years.

Rainbow trout hide in cold mountain streams
under natural cover. Where once was a door
is now a plaster wall, as if my father
never existed—my chest, an empty room

I don't recognize. Fishing reels were made
with Bakelite and the pipe stem clenched in

my father's teeth when he phones me,
his voice cloudy. I press my ear to
the receiver—he wears bright

colors—to catch every word,
hold my breath for fear (parallel
lines don't always stay

parallel) of losing him,
fear my words
not reaching him.

When he wasn't dead
my chest was filled
with clear shaded water

and I was not brittle.

Rainbow Trout (O. mykiss) is a member of the salmon family.

LAUREL SZYMKOWIAK

Broken

Broken jewelry offends me.
I hate single earrings.
I throw them away
or put them in a little bag
for Goodwill.
About half the time
the mate shows up when it's too late.
Another little bag:
Maybe the pair will meet up at Goodwill.
Broken clasps,
pearls running like fat little madmen
all over the shiny floor.
Pins that stick into your skin
because the safety catch has disappeared.
And stones, fallen out of rings,
ugly craters left behind.
There's a reproach there:
That which was precious,
you couldn't protect.
That which was precious,
you couldn't keep.

Cry for Mercy on Death Row

Inspired by "Just Mercy" by Bryan Stevenson

The silent screams, Black inmates
banging tin cups on their prison bars
showing fear, anger, disapproval, it's
time for an execution.

He sings "The Old Rugged Cross
So Despised By The World" as
he is strapped in the electric chair.
Smiles, thanks, good-bye to his lawyer

who feels he failed him, knows it's bias, a
miscarriage of justice, then a violent shake,
lights blinking on—off, smell of burning flesh,
refuses to scream, a botch—extreme pain.

Until he dies. In an electric chair, gas chamber,
by lethal injection, suffocation or depletion of
oxygen, administered until death. A legacy of
slavery continues in criminal justice systems.

Again we pray—please, please, mercy,
        M – E – R – C – Y.

Doris Miller Denied the Medal of Honor

After visiting Pearl Harbor

They called him "Dorie."
The guide said: *If you name a boy a girl's name—*
he has to learn to fight his way through life.
When the USS West Virginia was torpedoed in 1941,

this 6-foot-3 navy cook loaded the 50 caliber
anti-machine gun—began firing at the Japanese aircraft.
Blacks were not commissioned to use firearms.
Dorie was fighting mad—saved his torpedoed ship.

The Navy did not recognize *the unnamed Negro.*
The Pittsburgh Courier published his feat, kept his story
visible. Awards, accolades followed, elevated to Ship's
Cook Third Class. Dorie—first Black to earn the Navy Cross

for his heroic attack on the fleet in Pearl Harbor—
Dec. 7, 1941. Never an officer. Promoted to Mess
Attendant First Class. His parents were informed
in 1943: Dorie—*Missing in Action.*

Sexy Night in Saran Wrap

"I'll be home before you know it," my husband Bill assures me from a phone in the Pittsburgh airport. "I just have to catch the commuter to Morgantown in about 30 minutes."

"Great. I can't wait, two weeks is way too long. Besides, I want to hear about Germany and what the corporate world is really like."

"See you soon, honey."

With that our brief conversation ends and I can hardly wait to put my "Welcome Home" plan in action. I'd recently read a book by Maribel Morgan called *The Total Woman* on how to make and keep the excitement in one's marriage. I prepare to execute one of her strategies.

First I go upstairs to draw some bath water, making certain I put in appropriate amounts of bubbles and bath oil. After all, I want my skin to be as soft and supple as possible. After soaking in the bath, I apply body lotion liberally. Next I apply my makeup and the false eyelashes I'd purchased at the last minute to add a bit more glamour to the look. Earlier in the day I'd brought up the pink saran wrap I bought at the grocery store for this occasion and a pair of scissors, items I would need to create my sexy sarong.

Soon I begin the process of creating the perfect pink sarong. For more than thirty minutes, I busy myself with the cutting and wrapping necessary to create the perfect look while covering only the torso of my body. I'm exhausted but excited as I anticipate the reunion.

Not bad, I think as I add one more piece to this creation, a wide, pink saran bow, cut to fit around the middle of my breasts, attempting to enhance that sexy part of my feminine body. Next, I remove the large barrette holding my long hair up, so that it'll flow gently around my shoulders, and I brush it quickly. After all, I'm almost out of time before Bill arrives. Finally, I drench myself in Chanel No. 5, my favorite cologne. Earlier in the day I'd painted my nails an appropriate shade of sexy red. Grabbing my peek-a-boo spike heels from the closet, I head downstairs to finish my preparations.

I still need to put the finishing touches on the things from the kitchen. Putting the champagne on ice, I grab two champagne glasses from the china cabinet and place them on the counter. Putting the crackers and cream cheese on a china plate, I open the jar of caviar (another extravagance this young teacher and her husband can ill afford). I justify this purchase by saying to myself this is a huge and important occasion for us. After all, we're celebrating his homecoming and his first new professional job.

Now I'm ready for the big moment. I just have to wait for Bill to call from the Morgantown airport, alerting me that he's about 20 minutes away. Soon the call comes: "I've arrived, honey, I'll see you in a flash."

I am more than excited than ever now, anticipating his eminent arrival.

I light more candles, turn out all but one soft light in the entry hall, put the appetizer on the coffee table and the peek-a-boo spikes on my feet. I pour the two glasses of champagne and practice holding my glass appropriately by the stem. Finally, I'm ready; Bill should be arriving momentarily.

The doorbell rings. My heart pounds with excitement. Holding the champagne glass in one hand and unlatching the lock in the other, I quickly open the door. There standing before me—not Bill, but our very shocked middle-aged neighbor Bob—returning some borrowed tools. Embarrassed, I drop my expensive champagne goblet on the flagstone floor of the entry, shattering it. I slam the door in Bob's face. I begin crying as I pick up the broken shards of glass from the floor. At this same time, Bill is pulling in the driveway, but I don't realize it. I am deep in my pity party, complete with tears and broken glass.

As Bill opens the door, there I am in my "fancy" pink saran-wrap sarong on the floor, crying hysterically. As I'm telling him the story, the phone rings. It's Bob's wife, relating the same event amid gales of laughter. Bill gets off the phone, and amid his own gales of laughter, he hugs and reassures my embarrassed self.

Soon afterwards, I go upstairs and cut the "dress" off my body. I change into something a whole lot more comfortable and go down to continue our happy reunion.

Lost in Homewood Cemetery

Trees abound, red, yellow, nut-brown,
climbing hills, covering vales, sheltering
enclaves of monuments with names
such as McCormick, O'Hara, Fitzgerald
clustered together in one sector, Triola,
Fellini, Valenti, in another. Schwartz,
Klein, Goldstein are in the Star of David
section, for which I am searching.

In the not too distant future, a pink granite
marker, engraved with our name—WALD,
will be located there, between two oak trees.
I drive up and down hills, pass a jogger,
admire the foliage, stop to let squirrels
cross the road. Neither plot nor exit is in
sight. As I motor on and on, I imagine
an owl ruminating in one of our trees.

.

Omen

A month after he was admitted
to Charles Morris Rehabilitation Center
my husband phoned me for the first time.

He wanted me to bring all the old wrist-
watches that were in a drawer of his desk.

I did as he asked. The watches, there were six,
were all stopped—their batteries dead.

He told me, *I have a feeling of apprehension,*
that something bad is going to happen.

He died that night.

Winter Storm Jonas

I miss you
when I'm listening to "Ashes to Ashes"
like the first time I got ready to meet you in Midtown,
after painting my lips red

I'm happy, hope you're happy too…

which would later become familiar with your mouth—
the bite of a cheaper lager and overpriced Marlboro Reds
you bought from a corner store in Chinatown
not long before I pinned you against the ice-clad Confucius statue.

Imitation idea:
Grandma and Ziggy Stardust Fistfight in Heaven.
I'm not certain Sherman Alexie was a Bowie fan,
the only song you know from that album is "Starman"
and you never even met Grandma.

I miss the inebriated snow angels
and swilling wine during the blizzard,
trying to come up with our own satirical aphorisms
me interrupting you with an off-key cover—

Ashes to ashes, funk to funky.
We know Major Tom's a junkie.
Strung out in heaven's high
Hitting an all-time low

despite *my mouth* tasting like that on sale Yellow Tail
a selection Confucius himself criticized us for
suggesting that next time we opt for a drink more intuitive,
such as a refined Malbec from Buenos Aires,
or perhaps Southern France.

Lessens

Look back and your idol's name
has an asterisk in the record book.

Your first crush had a risible hairdo
and visibly caked makeup.

That doesn't mean you should have
buyer's remorse.

The moon colony shut down
but you computed an arc tangent, cashed out.

The guy who gave back his medals
pedals ahead of you in your furious cycles.

The author whose depleted fame spurred you
to emulation has lines that stir you still.

Sight on the red pennant or the green light
so long as it's upward or onward. Or the Cross.

ARLENE WEINER

Parking Parallel, for a Friend Whose Work Has Come to Nothing

Tight spot, busy narrow street,
behind a pickup truck, wide.
Stop anyway, line up, go into reverse—
traffic behind me pressing: *hurry*.
Turn the wheel hard, hard,
inch back, swing out,
slow & worried,

glance up: guy idling
high on the library steps
gestures with both hands,
twist, twist, come on, come on.
Finish cleanly at the curb,
no scrape or bump,
step out, lock up—
wave at my fan: *Olé!*

Averted eyes

Everything turns pink on my lips
hyacinth, apple core   —pursed
like a night train entering a tunnel

a distant sound barely heard
over the smooth gliding of
metal and flesh

Your mouth can be a shark too
moving silently through
threadbare seas of uncertainty

everything turns pink on my lips
except the unanswered words
oozing like a wound between us

tongue tree, white fangs,
night of sand and water, listening
this is the place of slow entry

and detention, tunnel of flesh
where skin may harbor
more silence than words

Every Day

Every day
          a small piece of me,
and a white page
a small piece,
          and waiting
a white page,
          and silence

every day
          a page
waiting for me
          every day
white
          like a shadow,
a small piece
          and me,
invisible
riding on a white shadow

me
          a small piece of time
with eyes closed
          and the page
wide open
          a small memory of time.

Loulouthia

Darkness settled hours past,
the night air close and warm
I trudge the small hill to my car
weary, yet awake
the pleasant effect of Jack Daniels
and good company

I pause to unlock the door
Soft pink petals against smooth glass
catch my eye
two roses gently tucked
under the windshield wiper
I sigh and smile
with the knowledge
of whose small hands
placed them there

Invisible

Pat filled her nostrils with the warmth of garbanzo and broccoli soup. It smelled delicious, and the weather outside was frightful, 15° and windy. If only when Stan came home he'd greet her with something besides, "What's for dinner?" Like how cute she looked in an apron. As if. The door opened. Stan. He looked right at her, but it seemed to Pat that he looked through her. "What's for dinner?" he asked loudly.

"Soup."

He continued to look through her, then unexpectedly said, "Are you in the basement? Be right there."

He took two steps, opened the basement door and pattered down. Puzzled, she stood where she was. Whatever. She felt tired. They'd been married for 30 years; were all couples that lasted this long so unemotional?

She frowned. Suddenly, she made up her mind, took a notepad from the drawer, scribbled *Grocery shopping* on it, and put the pad on the table. She grabbed coat, mittens, and scarf, and slipped out the back door, grateful that it closed quietly.

Once outside, she couldn't decide where to go. Starting the car was too noisy. Instead, she walked down Chestnut Street, feeling the bitter wind on her face but not her body; the mittens and scarf were fuzzy enough. She found herself standing outside the apartment building three doors down, where a young couple named José and Tekva lived. They'd been married for six months, and they always greeted Pat and Stan when they walked their French bulldog, *Bouffant.*

What was it like for these young people? Curious, she entered the building and headed to the door that led to the top floor. She gently twisted the knob. Unlocked, as they claimed it always was. The couple had told them that they never locked it, since the only people they locked out were themselves.

She crept up their steps, entered a hallway, and peeped into the kitchen. Twitched her nose in delight. Soup here too, smelling savory. Probably Tekva's specialty—cabbage, onion, and caraway. Tekva stood stirring the pot, her head turned toward a round table in their tiny kitchen where José sat, strumming his guitar and singing a song about a rose in Spanish Harlem.

Such a sweet couple! He from New Mexico, she from Pittsburgh, Squirrel Hill, yet a match made in heaven, Pat thought. She watched José, his eyes unfocused, as they often were when he played. Pat stood in his direct line of vision, but he no more saw her than Stan had. Then the music distracted her. Melancholy. She looked at Tekva, who cried over the soup as José finished the song. He looked at her and looked again.

"What is it, querida?" he asked softly.

"Oh José." Tekva gulped. Her head swiveled around as if to see if anyone were there to observe them, and not seeing Pat, she turned her gaze to his.

"Is there another woman?" she asked softly.

"What would make you—"

"Something in the pathos of the song makes me worry." Pat bit her lip. This was not, maybe, a scene she wanted to see.

José studied the floor. Then he looked up, his luminous eyes on his woman. "You've always known about my other love," he said in his soft tenor.

Tekva stirred the soup. She wiped her eyes and turned off the burner. Walked to stand behind José, her hands on his shoulder. "I know about your muse," she said, and surprised Pat by chuckling. "I didn't mean the music, my love. I meant, a human woman?"

He reached back and took her hands. "There is a human woman," he answered in his melodious voice. "The only woman for me. And she's right here with me in the kitchen." He stood up and turned around to take her in his arms.

Tekva collapsed against his broad chest. Then she squinted toward the hall. "Is someone there?"

"Only your ghosts, mi amor," he said, kissing her neck. "Your ghosts always pursue us, but we'll ignore them. Hoy, mañana y para siempre."

Pat turned to descend the steps. Had she stayed a second longer, she might've looked into Tekva's eyes to see her looking back, actually *seeing* her. That wouldn't do. Back down, out the front door. Walked home and came in noisily. "I didn't go to the store. Forgot what I wanted, came back to enjoy soup with my sweet husband."

Stan was setting out bowls, plates, silverware and napkins. "Hey! I came home and, damn! No girlfriend. Thanks for calling me sweet. I think I *could* be sweet on a frigid night." He grinned. "Any hot plans later?"

Pat strolled to the table and sat down. "What you see is what you get."

Richard Edward Taylor

a young man with Down Syndrome, goes to the movies with his aide.

After the film she goes to get the car. He wanders back inside.

Theater manager shouts, *Pay or get out*. Richard yells *No*, can't pay,

won't leave. Aide returns, tells the manager,

> *He has a disability,   he'll calm down, just give him some time.*

Manager can't wait, must keep the schedule, calls security. Three officers arrive.

Richard refuses to leave. Aide pleads,

> *He has a disability,   he'll calm down, just give him some time.*

Officers ignore her, move to physically remove him. Richard resists,

starts crying for his *mommy*, officers push him to the ground,

keep him on the ground, on his stomach, handcuff him from behind.

> Richard stops crying for his mommy.
> Richard stops resisting.
> Richard stops breathing.

Theater, now a crime scene, film schedule delayed, the body removed,

as the aide whispers,

> *He has a disability, he would've calmed down, if you just gave him some time.*

BARBARA WOLVOVITZ

Sperm Shopping

At the sperm bank, you get a catalogue
to find the biological father of your future child.

Each donor numbered—10, 350, 420—blond hair, brown,
blue eyes, tall, short, athletic, college graduate, race.

Choose the traits for the perfect baby for your family.
In 2010, Samantha and Ellen ordered No. 480, got 460.

They ordered white. They got black.
You can't return a baby to the sperm bank,
can't even get your money back. (No money back guarantee?)

In their white neighborhood, they can't get
Claire's hair done right, must drive her to a black salon.

In their small Midwestern town, they don't want
her stigmatized by her white classmates,

Samantha and Ellen will have to learn about black culture,
talk to black people. Sued the sperm bank for wrongful birth,

for money, for the emotional distress this has
and will cause them in the future.

Dying Clean

Let me burrow,
run arms and legs
along smooth, clean sheets.

Let me feel only this comfort.

Sun pierces sheer curtains,
exposes a fresh blank page—

while I try not to think
about clothes in the washer
souring with time,
or the thick dusty coat
covering my furniture.

Let me not picture the guest beds
quilted with piles of too-small clothes,
nor the unopened envelopes
screaming *IMPORTANT TAX DOCUMENT*
collecting on the floor by my desk.

There's an old New England custom
of keeping one's house *dying clean*.
Imagine everything spotless,
lying here without worrying
what my grown children would find.

Now I remember a stack of photo boxes
knocked over last week.
The avalanche still sits in the middle of the floor.

Last night I looked forward
so I took to bed early,
no late night wine
to cost me the morning.

Still, today I lie here,
craving comfort,
while the promising sun
wastes itself on me.

The Earrings, 1957

Leaving for a PTA meeting,
you're wearing the earrings.
Bright red.

You, my movie star mother:
bottle blonde,
short sleeved pullover sweater,
slitted straight skirt and heels.

But you, in those earrings I made
in Girl Scouts,
a Christmas craft:

dry, hard grains of rice,
glued together in a ball
stuck to a round metal earring base with a screw back,

painted with countless coats of red nail polish
to look like petals on a chrysanthemum.
Eight years old, standing in my nightgown
in our living room on Berkshire Drive,

I knew the flower earrings
looked like rice, painted red.
You insisted you loved them,
head high, back straight
as you walked out that door.

DIANE ZEBRINE

A Woman from the Infant Mortality Review Board Calls

No, I am not an addict.
Yes, I had a doctor.
No, we are not smokers.
No, I do not want you
coming to our home.

You could see it
on the sonogram's
chalk sketch, the club-
foot and cleft palate,
fingers like vines.
Some extra ones.
A one-in-ten-thousand
error of cell division,
the specialist said.
Most women
miscarry before it gets
this far.

Thirty hours
after the pitocin
and morphine,
after the resident
shoved his gloved
fist into me
to ripen my cervix
with a kelp stick,
I gave birth
to a shiny bruised
doll, small enough
to fit into a wicker
Easter basket
and whose silence
was welcome.

AMANDA NEWELL
2015 PATRICIA DOBLER POETRY AWARD WINNER

About the 2015 Patricia Dobler Poetry Award Winner

AMANDA NEWELL's work has appeared in *Bellevue Literary Review*, *Pearl*, *Pembroke Magazine*, *Poet Lore*, *Tar River Poetry*, and *War, Literature & the Arts*. She has been awarded scholarships from the Bread Loaf Writers' Conference, The Frost Place, and the Virginia Center for the Creative Arts. She chairs the English department at The Gunston School in Centreville, MD, and is pursuing her MFA at Warren Wilson College.

About the 2015 Patricia Dobler Poetry Award Judge

LYNN EMANUEL is the author of five books of poetry: *The Nerve of It, Poems New and Selected*; *Noose and Hook*; *Then Suddenly—*; *The Dig*; and *Hotel Fiesta*. Her work has been featured in the *Pushcart Prize Anthology* and *The Best American Poetry* numerous times and is included in *The Oxford Book of American Poetry*. She is the recipient of two fellowships from the National Endowment for the Arts, the National Poetry Series Award, the Eric Matthieu King Award from the Academy of American Poets, and, most recently, a fellowship from the Ranieri Foundation.

About the Patricia Dobler Poetry Award

This contest is open to women writers over the age of 40 who are U.S. citizens or permanent residents, currently living in the U.S., who have not published a full-length book of poetry, fiction, or non-fiction (chapbooks excluded). Current Carlow students or employees are not eligible.

The winner receives the Patricia Dobler Poetry Award, valued at $2,000, in the form of $1,000; round-trip travel, lodging, a reading at Carlow University in Pittsburgh with the final judge; and publication in *Voices from the Attic*.

Poems must be unpublished, up to 75 lines or fewer per poem; up to two poems, of any style, per submission.

All entrants receive a copy of *Voices from the Attic*.

For information on the Patricia Dobler Poetry Award, or Carlow University's Madwomen in the Attic program, please visit www.carlow.edu/Dobler_Poetry_Award.aspx or contact Jan Beatty or Sarah Williams-Devereux at 412.578.6346 or sewilliams412@carlow.edu.

Notes

"I haunt the edges of my past," by Susan Shaw Sailer, page 98, contains the phrase "the darkness in a stone" comes from Tom Sleigh's poem "KM4," section 7, "Rap," *Station Zed*.

"O. mykiss," by Laurel Syzmkowiak, page 119: Rainbow Trout (*O. mykiss*) is a member of the salmon family.

About the Madwomen

LISA ALEXANDER holds an MFA in Poetry from Drew University. A finalist for the 2016 *Tupelo Quarterly* Prize in Poetry, her work has also appeared or is forthcoming in various journals including *5 AM*, *BLOOM*, and *The Burnside Review*. She is a sound engineer for *Prosody*, NPR-affiliate WESA's weekly show featuring the work of national writers.

EILEEN ARTHURS' short stories have appeared in Carlow University's *10/ten* anthology, and *Sixfold Journal*. Her novel, *Lorelei's Family*, is available through Amazon. She is a charter member of the local writing group, The Liars' Club.

JEN ASHBURN completed her MFA at Chatham University. She has work published or forthcoming in various journals, including *The MacGuffin*, *Chiron Review*, *Grey Sparrow*, *Lilliput Review*, *Nerve Cowboy*, the *Pittsburgh Post-Gazette*, and the anthology, *Words Without Walls*.

VALERIE BACHARACH conducts weekly poetry workshops with the women of Power House, a halfway house for women in recovery from drug and alcohol addiction. Her poetry has appeared or is forthcoming in *Pittsburgh City Paper*'s *Chapter and Verse*, *Uppagus*, *Pittsburgh Post-Gazette*, *U.S. 1 Worksheets*, and *Poetica*.

SAMANTHA BARRETT graduated from the University of Pittsburgh and received her MFA in creative writing at Carlow University. Her work has appeared in *365 Tomorrows*, GeekSmash. com, *10/ten*, *The Chaffey Review*, and *Crack the Spine*, and has been performed by Carlow University Theatre. She has curated the Saturday Night Stories Reading Series and the Madwomen in the Attic Fiction Workshop public readings. She writes fantasy, cross-genre, and murder mystery plays.

TESS BARRY (MA in English, University of Pittsburgh; MFA in creative writing/poetry, Carlow University) was shortlisted for the 2015 Manchester Poetry Prize (UK). Twice a finalist for *North American Review*'s James Hearst Poetry Prize and *Aesthetica* Magazine's (UK) Poetry Award, she was also shortlisted for the 2014 *Bridport* Poetry Prize (UK). Her poems recently appear in *Mudfish Vol.19*, *Cordite Poetry Review* (Australia), and *The Compass Magazine* (UK). She teaches literature and creative writing at Robert Morris University.

JOAN E. BAUER is the author of *The Almost Sound of Drowning* (Main Street Rag, 2008). Recent poems have appeared in *Chiron Review*, *Cider Press Review*, *Confrontation*, *Paterson Literary Review*, *Slipstream*, *Uppagus*, and *U.S. 1 Worksheets*. In 2007, she won the Earle Birney Poetry Prize from *Prism International*. Along with Jimmy Cvetic, she co-hosts and curates the Hemingway's Summer Poetry Series.

JENNIFER JACKSON BERRY's first full-length collection of poetry, *The Feeder*, is forthcoming from YesYes Books in late 2016. Her poems have appeared in journals such as *Booth*, *Harpur Palate*, *Moon City Review*, *Stirring*, and *Whiskey Island*. She is the editor-in-chief of *Pittsburgh Poetry Review* and an assistant editor for *WomenArts Quarterly Journal*.

MARY BIANCHI graduated from Florida International University with a BFA, and from Cornell University with an MFA. She is the author of a review of the Carnegie International 2004, in the *Erie Times-News*, November 2004.

CYNTHIA BIERY is a retired public elementary school teacher who credits the Western Pennsylvania Writing Project (WPWP) for much of her writing training. A 1988 Fellow of WPWP, she has also mentored other Madwomen in the Madwomen Mentorship Program.

GERRY ROSELLA BOCCELLA is an educator, designer, and arts advocate. She graduated from Carlow University (then Mount Mercy) in 1958. In 1994, she received the Carlow

Alumnae Service Award in the Arts, followed in 1996 by the Carlow Woman of Spirit® Award for her work in the arts with at-risk youth. Her poetry has been featured on the WESA radio show, *Prosody*, in the *Pittsburgh Post-Gazette*, and in *Pittsburgh City Paper*.

DORALEE BROOKS, a teacher-consultant with the Western Pennsylvania Writing Project, teaches in the Developmental Studies Department at the Community College of Allegheny County. Her poems have appeared in the *Pittsburgh Post-Gazette*, *Chapter and Verse*, *Eye Contact*, *Uppagus*, *Dos Passos Review*, and the *Pittsburgh Poetry Review*. She holds an MFA from Carlow University.

ANNETTE BURICK graduated from the Art Institute of Pittsburgh in 1976 and later taught visual communications there. She worked as a graphic designer and illustrator for most of her career and was formerly a greeting card designer for Hallmark Cards.

JENNIFER BURNAU has published in the *Pittsburgh Post-Gazette*, the *Pittsburgh City Paper* and the online journal, *Fickle Muses*. She has participated in readings for the Madwomen in the Attic at Carlow University and at *MadFridays* at Delanie's Coffee House. She teaches in the Pittsburgh Public Schools.

AMY MCKAY BUTLER, M.ED holds a BA in history from The College of Wooster, OH, where she earned honors on her senior thesis, later acccpted into the Franklin D. Roosevelt Presidential Library and Museum, NYC. A master's in counseling from the University of Pittsburgh led her to a twenty-five year career as a Licensed Professional Counselor. She has published for several newsletters including the PA Clinical Mental Health Association. She is working on a novel and writing poetry for a chapbook.

GAYLE R. CARROLL has been writing for 20 years. Her poems have appeared in *The Innisfree Poetry Journal* online, *Poet Lore*, and *The Comstock Review*. She won the 2008 Thomas Merton Poetry of the Sacred Award, and placed in the 2009 Robert Frost Foundation Poetry Prize.

SHEILA CARTER-JONES has been published in *Pennsylvania Review, Pittsburgh Quarterly, Pittsburgh City Paper, Tri-State Anthology, Crossing Limits, Blair Mountain Press, Flights*, and the *Cave Canem* anthology. Her manuscript *Three Birds Deep* was selected by Elizabeth Alexander as the 2011 winner of the Naomi Long Madgett Poetry Book Award; and her chapbook *Crooked Star Dream Book* was named runner-up for the 2013 New York Center for Book Arts Chapbook Contest. She is a fellow of Cave Canem, Callaloo, and a 2015 Walter Dawkins Fellow of the Sewanee Writer's Conference.

CJ COLEMAN, a 2000 Western Pennsylvania Writing Project Fellow, has worked for the Pittsburgh Public Schools since 1990. She teaches 5th- and 6th-grade creative writing at the Pittsburgh Gifted Center, and has co-directed the WPWP Summer Institute for Teachers since 2003. Her work has been published in *Pittsburgh City Paper*'s *Chapter and Verse*.

REBECCA COLE-TURNER, PhD, CJN, is ordained as a minister in the United Church of Christ. She serves as Minister of Spiritual Formation at Smithfield UCC. Also a spiritual director, she is a Companion of Julian of Norwich (CJN). Her poetry has been published in *Hungry Hearts* and the *Pittsburgh Theological Seminary Journal*.

KAY COMINI's poetry has been published in *Poet Lore, Pittsburgh City Paper*, the *Pittsburgh Post-Gazette*; and the anthologies *Dark Side of the Moon, Voices from the Parlor*, and the Sandburg-Livesay anthology, *No Choice But to Trust*. Her chapbook, *The Picking Room*, placed second in the White Eagle Coffee Press contest. She is a retired welfare caseworker and an energy healer.

ANGELA CORNELIUS is a poetry student in the MFA program at Carlow University. She has a creative consulting business and is a graphic and web design freelancer. She received her MA in digital art from Maryland Institute College of Art. Her poetry has appeared in *Rune*, Robert Morris University's literary journal.

ELISABETH CRAGO is a student in the MFA program at Carlow University, writing poetry and creative non-fiction. A graduate of Lehman College, CUNY and the University of Michigan, she has undergraduate degrees in English and nursing and a graduate degree in nursing. She directed the Breast Program at Lehigh Valley Hospital in Allentown, PA. She then spent 12 years in New Zealand involved in farming and aquaculture. She is also a volunteer mentor at the Women in Transition program of Center for Women.

ANN CURRAN is author of three books of poetry: *Placement Test* (Editor's Choice, Main Street Rag), *Me First* (Lummox Press) and *Knitting the Andy Warhol Bridge* (Lummox Press). Three poems in *Knitting* appeared originally in *The New York Times*.

SARA DAVIS is the author of the chapbook *Spent*, published by Finishing Line Press in 2014. She is a retired English teacher and a member of the Western Pennsylvania Writing Project. Her poetry has been published in *Lavanderia: a Mixed Load of Women, Wash, and Word* (City Works Press), *Riverspeak*, *Threads*, *Broad River Review* (for which she was a finalist for the Rash Award), the *Pittsburgh Post-Gazette*, and *Evening Street Review*.

VICTORIA DYM is the author of the chapbook, *Class Clown*, published by Finishing Line Press. She is a graduate of Ringling Bros. Barnum & Bailey Clown College. She holds a BA in philosophy from the University of Pittsburgh, and an MFA in creative writing (poetry) from Carlow University. She lives in Tampa, Florida.

DONNA DZURILLA has creative nonfiction published in the *Pittsburgh Post-Gazette*, *The Critical Point*, and the anthology *Dionne's Story, Volume II*. She graduated from Carlow College in 2002 with a BA in professional writing and will enter Point Park University's MFA program in playwriting and screenwriting. Several of her monologues have been performed by Carlow University Theatre.

ALICE FUCHS, a Madwoman since the mid-eighties, has worked towards an MFA at the University of Pittsburgh. She has published three novels as e-books and is working on a fourth. She has also published three poetry chapbooks: *Morning in Agrigento*, *Blood Poppies*, and *god L*.

KATHLEEN FURBEE's poetry, short stories, and essays have been published in several literary journals and anthologies including *Kestrel*, *The Anthology of Appalachian Writers*, and *Fed from the Blade*. She received a West Virginia artist fellowship in 2008, placed second in the West Virginia Fiction Competition in 2015, and placed first in the WV Writer's Contest for her novel, *Frogs*. She is part of the workshop taught by Lori Wilson in Morgantown, West Virginia.

BRI GRIFFITH is a junior creative writing major at Carlow University with two minors in professional writing and communications. She is the emcee for the Red Dog Reading Series, Editor-in-Chief for *The Carlow Chronicle*, and a student writing intern for *Study Breaks Magazine*. Her poems have appeared in *The Critical Point*, *Rune*, *Pittsburgh Poetry Review*, and *The 6th Anniversary ITWOW Anthology*.

ALEXIS HARRELL is a creative writing major at Carlow University with minors in women's studies and philosophy. She believes that Carlow has played a tremendous role in helping her find her voice through poetry. She plans to continue her education in the MFA in Creative Writing Program at Carlow.

PAT HART writes plays, short stories, and novels. Her playwriting credits include *Book Wench*, performed at the 2015 Strawberry One-Act Festival, New York, NY. Her published short stories include "The Vigil," *The Writing Disorder* (Fall 2015); and "Spider Ball," *Rune* (May 2015). She is the founder of the Free Association Reading Series.

JANET INNAMORATO received a BA from the University of California at Los Angeles in 1977 and a Juris Doctor from the University of Pittsburgh School of Law in 1980.

ALEXANDRA KEMRER's poems have appeared in *Pittsburgh City Paper's Chapter and Verse*. She also contributed to the *Lent 2016 Daily Reflections in the Jubilee Year of Mercy*, a journal published by Carlow University.

JILL KHOURY is the author of two chapbooks: *Borrowed Bodies* (Pudding House, 2009), and *Chance Operations* (Paper Nautilus, 2016). Her full-length collection, *Suites for the Modern Dancer*, is forthcoming from Sundress Publications in 2016. She holds an MFA from The Ohio State University, and edits the journal, *Rogue Agent*. She is interested in the intersection of poetry, visual art, gender, and disability.

KARA KNICKERBOCKER received her BA in English from Westminster College in 2012. Her poetry and creative nonfiction has been published or is forthcoming in *The Blue Route*, *Scrawl*, *The Original Magazine*, *Pittsburgh Poetry Review*, and *Longridge Review*. She works at Carnegie Mellon University.

GAIL LANGSTROTH is a poet, eurythmist, and international stage artist who received her MFA in Poetry from Drew University. She is the winner of the 2011 Patricia Dobler Poetry Award. Her poems have appeared in *Citron*, *Clay Bird Review*, *Clementine*, *Passager*, *Rune*, *Rust + Moth*, and *Yemassee*. In May 2016, Langstroth releases her film, *In & & &*. Her latest eurythmy production, *Tormentos de Paz*, premieres with percussionist/vocalist Fred Johnson in Barcelona in July 2016.

MICHELLE MAHER is a professor of English at La Roche College. Maher won the 2012 Patricia Dobler Poetry Award, a national contest sponsored by Carlow University. Her poem, "At the Brera, Milan," was selected from 380 poems by judge Toi Derricotte. Her work has appeared in journals such as the *Chautauqua Literary Journal, The Georgetown Review, Atlanta Review*, and *U.S. 1 Worksheets*.

MJNAREY is new to the Madwomen community. This is her first published poetry.

MAEVE MURRAY has an MFA in creative writing from Carlow University, and her short story, "Numbers," was published in the program's *10/ten* anthology as the winning piece of fiction. She has read her work at several public events, including Carlow University's 2014-2015 Graduate Colloquium and the Saturday Night Stories Reading Series. She also writes book reviews for *Coal Hill Review*, an online imprint of Autumn House Press.

TERESA NAREY earned her MFA in creative writing from Chatham University. Her poetry has appeared in *Connotations Press, No Tokens, Pittsburgh City Paper*, and *Wicked Alice*. She has been a featured guest on *Prosody*, NPR-affiliate WESA's weekly radio show featuring the work of national writers. She is a 2014 fellow of the Western Pennsylvania Writing Project.

MARILYN MARSH NOLL earned her MFA in creative writing (poetry) at American University in Washington, D.C., in 1994. She is the author of *Ordinary Bones*, published in 2016 by MadBooks. Her chapbook, *Thirteen Ways of Looking at Bones*, won the Pennsylvania Poetry Society Chapbook Award in 2007. Her children's book, *Jonathan and the Flying Broomstick* (Sunlight and Shadow Press), was published in 2010. Her poems have appeared in the *Comstock Review, Folio, Pittsburgh Post-Gazette, Potter's Wheel*, and *Uppagus*.

LIANE ELLISON NORMAN has published five books of poetry: *Breathing the West: Great Basin Poems, Roundtrip, Driving Near the Old Federal Arsenal, Keep*, and *The Duration of Grief*; individual poems in the *North American Review, Grasslimb, Come Together: Imagine Peace, Rune*, on *newversenews. com*, in the *Pittsburgh Post-Gazette*, and *Pittsburgh City Paper*. Her poem "Tree" was read by Garrison Keillor on the radio on December 3, 2012. She has also published a book about a local peace group, a biography, a novel, and many articles and essays. Her new book, *Way Station*, is forthcoming from Finishing Line Press.

LAURA SLOAN PATTERSON is an English professor at Seton Hill University. Her poetry has appeared or is forthcoming in *Absinthe Poetry Review* (as the issue's Green Hour Feature), *Sugared Water, Rust + Moth, HOOT, Spry, Pittsburgh Poetry Review, Not One of Us*, and *Mom Egg Review*. She holds a bachelor's degree from Princeton University and a master's and doctorate in English literature from Vanderbilt University.

DORINA PENA is the author of a chapbook, *Leaving the Tree*, published by Monkeyman Press. Individual poems are published in *Pittsburgh City Paper, Flare: the Flagler Review*, and *Girls with Glasses*. She is sending out her full-length manuscript, *Masking White*, and her second chapbook, *Black History*. She graduated from the University of Pittsburgh with her BA in English writing (poetry), and from Carlow University with her MFA in creative writing (poetry). She lives in Philadelphia, PA.

ANNE PICONE, a retired English teacher, is a member of the Pittsburgh Poetry Society and the Naples Florida Writer's Forum. Her poetry has appeared in *The Loyalhanna Review* and the *Pittsburgh Post-Gazette*.

MAEVE RAFFERTY recently relocated from her native Northern Ireland to Pittsburgh, where she has worked in urban forestry and community gardening. She graduated in 1999 with a BS in environmental biology at University College Dublin, and has worked in the field of nature conservation in Northern Ireland for more than ten years. She has been experimenting with memoir essays and fiction.

LAURA J. ROOP is the director of the Western Pennsylvania Writing Project, a National Writing Project site at the University of Pittsburgh School of Education. While a graduate student at the University of Michigan, she won two Major Hopwood Awards (poetry and essay), as well as the Cowden, Gutterman, Rapaport, and Academy of American Poetry prizes.

SUSAN SHAW SAILER is the author of *Ship of Light* (Port Yonder Press), and a chapbook, *Coal* (Finishing Line Press). Her second book, *The God of Roundabouts*, is forthcoming from Word Press. Her recent poems have appeared or are forthcoming in *Pittsburgh Poetry Review*, *Sugared Water*, and *Rose Red Review*. She lives in West Virginia.

JOANNE MATONE SAMRANEY authored two poetry chapbooks, *Grounded Angels*, winner of the 2001 Acorn-Rukeyser Chapbook Award, and *Remaking Driftwood*. Her manuscript, *Believe the Leaves*, was a finalist in the Panhandler and Perivale poetry chapbook contests. She co-authored *Breaking Bread with the Boscos*, a family memoir and cookbook; read her work on National Public Radio's *Prosody*; was part of *Tea Time Ladies*, a performance poetry group; and served on the International Poetry Forum's Associates' Board.

KAREN SANTELLI is a writer and educator whose undergraduate training was as a journalist. She has taught writing at The Art Institute of Pittsburgh and Shady Side Academy.

KAYLA SARGESON is the author of the chapbooks *Mini Love Gun* (Main Street Rag, 2013) and *BLAZE* (Main Street Rag, 2015). She is the poetry editor for *Pittsburgh City Paper's Chapter and Verse*.

ELIZABETH NADAS SEAMANS is a writer and filmmaker who worked with PBS television artist Fred Rogers as scriptwriter, filmmaker, actor, and producer for 35 years. Children and American traditional life are her primary subject matters. She has received support from the Smithsonian Institution, the National Endowment for the Arts, and the Heinz Foundation. Her work has been screened on PBS, the Museum of Modern Art, the National Gallery, and the Pittsburgh Center for the Arts.

JANICE E. SEIGLE holds a BA in both writing and music from Carlow University and a master's degree in public management from Carnegie Mellon University's Heinz College. An avid gardener, several of her gardening articles have been published. She is a recipient of the Western Pennsylvania Press Club's Golden Quill Award in the home and gardening category.

BARBARA SHEMA has facilitated poetry workshops with the Women's Shelter of Pittsburgh, adult literacy students in Providence, Rhode Island, and art workshops with refugees in Providence. Her artwork is represented by Gallerie CHIZ on Ellsworth Ave.

SUE ANN SIMAR is a member of the West Virginia Madwomen in the Attic group led by Lori Wilson. She has published work in *Backbone Mountain Review*, and she works in health care.

M.A. SINNHUBER's chapbook, *The Leaving Field*, was published by MadBooks in 2013. She was the recipient of a scholarship to the Ligonier Valley Writers' Conference. She has had a career in public television and is a visual artist in Pittsburgh. She has been published in the *Pittsburgh Post-Gazette* and *Pittsburgh City Paper*.

SYLVIA J. SMITH has worked at Carnegie Mellon University for the last 36 years. At age 55, she decided to follow her first love—writing—and later enrolled in the Madwomen in the Attic workshops. She is a Pittsburgh native.

ELISABETH SUTOR studies writing at the University of Pittsburgh, after a previous stint in the aftermarket book industry. She is working on a novel.

LAUREL SZYMKOWIAK has been published in several journals, including *Pretty Owl, U.S. 1 Worksheets, Rune, Perihelion*, and *The Del Sol Review*.

REBECCA TAKSEL's novel, *Come Away*, was published by Little Feather Books in 2016. Her nonfiction appeared regularly between 2004 and 2014 in the *Redwood Coast Review*, where she was contributing editor. She has written on interior design for *Natural Home* and on animal protection for *Animals Agenda Magazine*.

BEATRICE W. VASSER is the author of the chapbook, *The Color of Black* (MadBooks, 2015), and *The Circle of Life: Verses From My Journey* (Pneuma Publishing, Inc, 2008). Her work has been published in *HeART*; *Dionne's Story, Vol. II*; *Pittsburgh City Paper*; and the Victorian Ministries website. She is a retired teacher, athletic director, and professional counselor. She received her PhD from the University of Pittsburgh.

BETH VOLTZ grew up in Wheeling, West Virginia and graduated from West Virginia University with a bachelor's in English and master's in English education. As an English teacher at West Allegheny High School, she spearheaded a committee that integrated writing across the curriculum. In 1995, she became a Fellow of the Western Pennsylvania Writing Project, where she has served in several capacities including the Coordinator of the Young Writers Institute and teacher and co-director of the Writing Project.

LUCIENNE WALD has been published in the *Pittsburgh Post-Gazette, Living Inland*, and the *Leader Times*, an edition of the *Tribune-Review*. She has been attending the Madwomen in the Attic workshops for over 25 years. She has won awards from the Westmoreland County Arts & Heritage Festival, as well as the Pittsburgh Poetry Society.

MELINDA WARD graduated from Carlow University in 2012 with a BA in sociology and a minor in creative writing. She works as a family based mental health clinician with Every Child, Inc., a nonprofit in Pittsburgh. She has published several pieces related to social justice and politics in The Thomas Merton Center's *New People*.

ARLENE WEINER is the author of *Escape Velocity*, published by Ragged Sky Press. Her poems have been published in a variety of journals, including the *Paterson Literary Review, Pleiades*, and *Poet Lore*; and read by Garrison Keillor on *The Writer's Almanac*. She was awarded a residence at the MacDowell Colony. She is working on another manuscript, *City Bird*.

CAROLINA WILSON is a Chilean poet who received her BA from the University of Pittsburgh. Her poetry has been published in *The Exchange*, and *The University of Canberra International Poetry Prize 2015*.

RITA WILSON is a writer, artist, and educator whose work has been published in *Riverspeak* and *Rune*. Her oil paintings have won second place and People's Choice awards at the Annual West Hills Art League Shows. She received her MFA in creative writing from Carlow University in 2014. She teaches English and creative writing, and is finishing her first memoir.

CHRISTINE AIKENS WOLFE is the author of *Rise Up Singing*, a young adult novel; and *The Prince and the Thorny Wood*, a fairy tale. She is also the co-editor, with Matthew Luskey, of *The Poetic Classroom* (Autumn House Press), about how to tailor MFA-level creative writing assignments for grades kindergarten through college. Her short story, "Lipstick," won third place at the Westmoreland Arts and Heritage Festival in 2008. She attended the Western Pennsylvania Writing Project's summer institute in

1992, and now teaches young writers, usually at the University of Pittsburgh's Young Writers Institute.

BARBARA WOLVOVITZ's poems have been published in the *Pittsburgh Post-Gazette*, *Pittsburgh City Paper*'s *Chapter and Verse*, and *Rune*. Her work also received Honorable Mention in Seton Hill University's *Eye Contact* (Fall 2014 edition).

DIANE ZEBRINE holds degrees from Bethany College and Slippery Rock University. Retired from a career in education, she was an elementary school counselor and a teacher for Hampton Township and Shaler school districts, and Allegheny Intermediate Unit. She has taught parenting and other adult classes and led support groups. She also sings with The Pittsburgh Concert Chorale.

Madwomen History

The Madwomen in the Attic Writing Workshops, named after the groundbreaking study by Sandra Gilbert and Susan Gubar on the 19th-century woman writer, were founded in 1979 by Dr. Ellie Wymard after a campus visit by the writer, Tillie Olsen. When Olsen was mobbed by women with stories, poems, and questions, it became clear that there was a hunger and a need for women's stories to be told. Over the years, visiting writers such as Tess Gallagher, Maggie Anderson, Alicia Ostriker, Marita Golden, Naomi Shihab Nye, Judith Vollmer, Maxine Kumin, Toi Derricotte, Denise Duhamel, and Jean Valentine would arrive to feed this hunger. The workshops were originally taught by Ellie Wymard. Esteemed fiction writer Jane Candia Coleman was the first director of the Madwomen, and later the beloved poet Patricia Dobler directed and developed the Madwomen in the Attic Workshops until her death in 2004. Patricia Dobler dedicated many years of her working life to the Madwomen to create an inclusive, vibrant atmosphere where women of varied backgrounds could meet and study the craft of writing. For this the Madwomen will be forever grateful.

About Patricia Dobler

Patricia Dobler was born in Middletown, Ohio, in 1939. She is the author of *UXB* (Mill Hunk Books, 1991) and *Talking to Strangers* (University of Wisconsin Press, 1986), which won the Brittingham Prize in Poetry; a chapbook, *Forget Your Life*, was published by the University of Nebraska Press. She also completed a third full-length collection, titled *Now*. Her poems have appeared in such publications as *Mid-American Review*, *The Ohio Review*, *Ploughshares*, *Prairie Schooner*, and *Southern Poetry Review*. Her work has been anthologized in *A Gathering of Poets*, *A New Geography of Poets*, *The Carnegie Mellon Anthology of Poetry*, *Working Classics*, *Vital Signs*, *Anthology of Magazine Verse & Yearbook of American Poetry*, and others. She has received grants from the National Endowment for the Arts, the Pennsylvania Council on the Arts, fellowships from the Corporation of Yaddo and Villa Montalvo and a Pushcart Poetry prize. She lived in Pittsburgh, Pennsylvania, and taught for many years at Carlow University, where she directed the Women's Creative Writing Center, the Madwomen in the Attic Writing Workshops, and was instrumental in developing the MFA program. She died July 24, 2004. After her death, her *Collected Poems* was published by Autumn House Press in 2005.

The Editors

JAN BEATTY directs the Madwomen in the Attic writing workshops at Carlow University, where she is also director of creative writing and teaches in the low-residency MFA program. She is the author of five books of poetry, all published by the University of Pittsburgh Press. *Jackknife: New and Selected Poems*, is forthcoming in Spring, 2017. The *Switching/Yard*, 2013, won the 2014 Paterson Award for Literary Excellence. *Library Journal* named it one of ...*30 New Books That Will Help You Rediscover Poetry*. Beatty's work was featured in *The Huffington Post* as one of ten women writers for "required reading." Other books include *Red Sugar*, finalist for the 2009 Paterson Poetry Prize; *Boneshaker*, finalist for the Milt Kessler Award; and *Mad River*, winner of the Agnes Lynch Starrett Prize. Her chapbook, *Ravage*, was published by Lefty Blondie Press in 2012. Beatty's limited edition chapbook, *Ravenous*, won the 1995 State Street Prize.

Awards include a $10,000 Regional Artists Grant from the Pittsburgh Foundation, the $15,000 Creative Achievement Award from the Pittsburgh Cultural Trust, the Pablo Neruda Prize for Poetry, a finalist for the Discovery/*The Nation* Award, and two fellowships from the Pennsylvania Council on the Arts. Individual poems have appeared in journals such as *Poetry* and *Best American Poetry (2013)*. Her essays on writing have appeared in anthologies by Autumn House Press, *Creative Nonfiction*, and the State University of New York Press. She has been featured at venues such as Split This Rock and the Geraldine R. Dodge Festival. For 20 years, Beatty has hosted and produced *Prosody*, a public radio show on NPR-affiliate WESA-FM featuring national writers.

JOY KATZ is the author of three poetry collections, most recently *All You Do is Perceive*, a finalist for the National Poetry series, and named among the best books of 2013 by the *Kansas City Star*.

Honors for her work include fellowships from the National Endowment for the Arts and Stanford University's Wallace Stegner Program, a Pushcart prize, and a Pittsburgh Foundation individual artist grant for her work-in-progress about race and voice. She teaches in the MFA program at Chatham University and in the Madwomen in the Attic workshops.

NANCY KIRKWOOD teaches the Madwomen in the Attic nonfiction workshop. She holds a BA in creative writing from the University of Pittsburgh and an MFA in creative writing from Carlow University. She is an adjunct faculty member of Carlow University's English Department and also works as an independent editor and writing coach. Her honors include the Schuylkill County Arts Fellowship Award, and publications in *Literary Mama*, *Pittsburgh City Paper*, and *Girls with Glasses*.

NANCY KRYGOWSKI is the author of *Velocity* (University of Pittsburgh Press, 2007), winner of the 2006 Agnes Lynch Starrett Poetry Prize. Her poems have appeared in *Prairie Schooner*, *River Styx*, *Southern Poetry Review*, *5 AM*, and other magazines. She is the recipient of a Pennsylvania Council on the Arts Individual Artist Grant, a Pittsburgh Foundation grant, and awards from the Academy of American Poets and the Association of Writers & Writing Programs. She works as an adult literacy instructor.

EVELYN PIERCE teaches the Madwomen in the Attic fiction workshops. She has published short stories in *The Yoknapatawpha Review*, *Weave*, and *The SOMOS Anthology*. She also wrote the screenplay adaptations for Larry Brown's *Dirty Work* and Bernie MacKinnon's *Song for a Shadow*. She has taught writing since 1983, and is the recipient of multiple teaching honors. In 2004, she received the Sustained Excellence in Teaching Award at Carnegie Mellon University, where she teaches management communications. She received her MFA in fiction from the University of Pittsburgh.

ELLEN McGRATH SMITH teaches at the University of Pittsburgh and in the Carlow University Madwomen in the Attic program. Her writing has appeared in *The American Poetry Review*, *Los Angeles Review*, *Quiddity*, *Cimarron*, and other journals, and in several anthologies, including *Beauty Is a Verb: The New Poetry of Disability*. Smith has been the recipient of an Orlando Prize, an Academy of American Poets award, a Rainmaker Award from *Zone 3* magazine, and a 2007 Individual Artist grant from the Pennsylvania Council on the Arts. Her second chapbook, *Scatter, Feed*, was published by Seven Kitchens Press in the fall of 2014, and her book, *Nobody's Jackknife*, was published in 2015 by the West End Press.

SARAH WILLIAMS-DEVEREUX is a poet, educator, and transformative language artist. Her poetry has appeared in *Snapdragon: A Journal of Art & Healing*, *Sampsonia Way Magazine*, *Pittsburgh City Paper*, *Pittsburgh Love Stories*, and WESA-FM's *Prosody*. She leads poetry workshops for the Madwomen in the Attic. She is certified in Writing Group Leadership from Amherst Writers & Artists, and certified in Transformative Language Arts from the TLA Network.

LORI WILSON teaches a satellite Madwomen in the Attic poetry workshop in Morgantown, WV. She is the author of the poetry collection, *House Where a Woman* (Autumn House Press, 2009). Her poems have appeared in journals such as *Southern Poetry Review*, *Salamander*, *The Laurel Review*, *Georgetown Review*, and *Cimarron*; and in various anthologies including, most recently, *The Lake Rises: poems to & for our bodies of water* (Stockport Flats, 2013). Nominated for a Pushcart Prize and recipient of the Mid Atlantic Arts Foundation Creative

Fellowship at the Virginia Center for Creative Arts, Wilson holds an MA in economics from Harvard University and an MFA in poetry from Drew University.

*

LISA ALEXANDER holds an MFA in Poetry from Drew University. A finalist for the 2016 *Tupelo Quarterly* Prize in Poetry, her work has also appeared or is forthcoming in various journals including *5 AM*, *BLOOM*, and *The Burnside Review*. She is a sound engineer for *Prosody*, National Public Radio affiliate WESA's weekly show featuring the work of national writers.

TESS BARRY (MA in English, University of Pittsburgh; MFA in creative writing/poetry, Carlow University) was shortlisted for the 2015 Manchester Poetry Prize (UK). Twice a finalist for *North American Review*'s James Hearst Poetry Prize and *Aesthetica* Magazine's (UK) Poetry Award, she was also shortlisted for the 2014 *Bridport* Poetry Prize (UK). Her poems recently appear in *Mudfish Vol.19*, *Cordite Poetry Review* (Australia), and *The Compass Magazine* (UK). She teaches literature and creative writing at Robert Morris University.

BRI GRIFFITH is a junior creative writing major at Carlow University with minors in professional writing and communications. She is the emcee for the Red Dog Reading Series, Editor-in-Chief for *The Carlow Chronicle*, and a student writing intern for *Study Breaks Magazine*. Her poems have appeared in *The Critical Point*, *Rune*, *Pittsburgh Poetry Review*, and *The 6th Anniversary ITWOW Anthology*.

LIANE ELLISON NORMAN has published five books of poetry: *Breathing the West: Great Basin Poems*, *Roundtrip*, *Driving*

Near the Old Federal Arsenal, *Keep*, and *The Duration of Grief*;
individual poems in the *North American Review*, *Grasslimb*,
Come Together: Imagine Peace, *Rune*, on *newversenews.com*, in
the *Pittsburgh Post Gazette*, and *Pittsburgh City Paper*. Her poem
"Tree" was read by Garrison Keillor on the radio on December 3,
2012. She has also published a book about a local peace group, a
biography, a novel, and many articles and essays. Her new book,
Way Station, is forthcoming from Finishing Line Press.

Books of Note

BY PATRICIA DOBLER:

— *Collected Poems*, Autumn House Press, 2005.
— *UXB*, Mill Hunk Books, 1991.
— *Talking to Strangers*, University of Wisconsin Press,
  1986 Brittingham Prize in Poetry.
— *Forget Your Life*, chapbook, University of Nebraska Press, 1982.

BY JAN BEATTY:

— *Jackknife: New and Selected Poems*, forthcoming,
  University of Pittsburgh Press, 2017.
— *The Switching/Yard*, University of Pittsburgh Press, 2013.
— *Ravage*, chapbook, Lefty Blondie Press, 2012.
— *Red Sugar*, University of Pittsburgh Press, 2008.
— *Boneshaker*, University of Pittsburgh Press, 2002.
— *Mad River*, University of Pittsburgh Press, 1995.
— *Ravenous*, chapbook, State Street Press, 1995.

BY JOY KATZ:

— *All You Do is Perceive*, Four Way Books, 2013.
— *Dark Horses: Poets on Overlooked Poems*, co-editor,
  University of Illinois Press, 2007.
— *The Garden Room*, chapbook, Tupelo Press, 2006.
— *Fabulae*, Southern Illinois University Press, 2002.

BY NANCY KRYGOWSKI:

— *Velocity*, University of Pittsburgh Press, 2007.

BY LIANE ELLISON NORMAN:

— *Way Station*, forthcoming, Finishing Line Press, 2016.
— *Breathing the West: Great Basin Poems*, Bottom Dog Press, 2012.
— *Driving Near the Old Federal Arsenal*, chapbook,
   Finishing Line Press, 2011.
— *Keep*, Smoke & Mirrors Press, 2008.
— *The Duration of Grief*, Smoke & Mirrors Press, 2005.
— *Stitches in Air: A Novel About Mozart's Mother*,
   Smoke & Mirrors Press, 2001.
— *Hammer of Justice: Molly Rush and the Plowshares Eight*,
   PPI Books, 1990.

BY ELLEN MCGRATH SMITH:

— *Nobody's Jackknife*, West End Press, 2015.
— *Scatter, Feed*, chapbook, Seven Kitchens Press, 2014.
— *A Dog Makes His Rounds and Other Poems*, chapbook,
   Another Thing Press, 2002.

BY SARAH WILLIAMS-DEVEREUX:

— *Our Stories, Our Selves: A3P: The African American Arts Project:
   A Study of African American Young Adult Arts Participation*,
   with Annabelle Clippinger, PITT ARTS, University of
   Pittsburgh, 2006.

BY LORI WILSON:

— *House Where a Woman*, Autumn House Press, 2009.